The Way to P
National Curriculum
Maths

GCSE
Higher Level

Arnold Burdett

VERMILION
LONDON

First published in 1994

1 3 5 7 9 10 8 6 4 2

Text copyright © Rockhopper 1994

First published in the United Kingdom in 1994
by Vermilion
an imprint of Ebury Press
Random House, 20 Vauxhall Bridge Road,
London SW1V 2SA

Random House Australia (Pty) Limited
20 Alfred Street, Milsons Point, Sydney,
New South Wales 2061, Australia

Random House New Zealand Limited
18 Poland Road, Glenfield,
Auckland 10, New Zealand

Random House South Africa (Pty) Limited
PO Box 337, Bergvlei, South Africa

Random House UK Limited Reg. No. 954009

Editor: Alison Wormleighton
Design: Jerry Goldie Graphic Design

A CIP catalogue record for this book
is available from the British Library

ISBN 0-09-178127-2

Typeset by AFS Image Setters Ltd, Glasgow
Printed in Great Britain by Butler & Tanner Ltd,
London and Frome

Foreword

Welcome to THE WAY TO PASS MATHS GCSE HIGHER LEVEL. I want to tell you why I have put together this series of books, along with a team of teachers, advisers and examiners.

The fact that you are studying for the Higher Level paper in Maths means you must be reasonably comfortable with the subject – possibly even someone who loves Maths and wants to continue to study it in the future. I know that when I was taking my exams at your age I enjoyed every moment of Maths study, but I have also found over the years that the more help you have and the longer you spend on something, the more likely you are to get over any difficulties.

As you are studying for GCSE Maths Higher Level, you already know that you are aiming high, perhaps even a Grade A*, and it is obviously well worth trying for. Whatever you might think about school, and about Maths in particular, there is no doubt that Maths and English are the two most important subjects for you to do well in. If you understand most of what you're taught, you are set for a brighter future, being able to do some of the things you've always wanted to. THE WAY TO PASS can help you through your GCSE courses, making the subjects you're taught a little more understandable and interesting, making your exams easier and helping you to get the best grades possible.

All of the books are based around work for you to do at home. Most of the explanations will have been covered in classes at school and so you won't want to wade through pages and pages of more explanations. That is why in each section we give you a concise list of the main things you need to know, and then work through exercises to practise each one.

This completely new range of books has been organised so that, if you want to, you can follow the already successful VIDEO CLASS videos covering the same subjects/levels. All of the book sections work together neatly with the video sections so that you have a complete course at your fingertips. Alternatively, the books can be used on their own, without the videos.

I certainly hope that this series will make Maths and English more approachable and slightly friendlier than they were before. Remember, you must follow what is taught in school and do as many exercises as you can – the more practice you get, the better you will be.

Carol Vorderman

Contents

The National Curriculum

The National Curriculum sets targets for pupils of all abilities from age 5 to 16, specifying what they should know, understand and be able to do at each stage of their education. It is divided into four **Key Stages**: Key Stage 1 (age 5–7), Key Stage 2 (age 7–11), Key Stage 3 (age 11–14) and Key Stage 4 (age 14–16).

At the end of Key Stages 1, 2 and 3, pupils take national tests in the **core subjects**: Maths and English (at age 7, 11 and 14) and Science (at age 11 and 14). At the end of Key Stage 4 (age 16) the **GCSE examinations** are the main way of assessing children's progress.

Whereas in the tests at Key Stages 1, 2 and 3 children achieve particular **Levels**, moving up one Level every two years or so, in the GCSE examination they are graded from A (at the top) to G (at the lower end of the scale). The grade A* may be awarded for exceptional achievement. U stands for ungraded or unclassified.

Nearly all pupils take GCSE examinations in English and in Maths. There are different **tiers** of paper to suit the varying capabilities of the pupils, and the grading system reflects the difficulty of the papers taken. Teachers decide which level is best suited to each pupil, who then has a clearly defined target to aim for.

THE WAY TO PASS books are all based on National Curriculum requirements. The GCSE English book covers the main elements of the syllabus at each tier, while GCSE Maths is split into three different books – Foundation, Intermediate and Higher – corresponding to the three tiers of the examination papers. The books will serve as a valuable back-up to a child's classwork and homework and provide an excellent preparation for the GCSE examinations.

Introduction

When preparing for a GCSE examination in Mathematics, it is important that you structure your revision. THE WAY TO PASS MATHS GCSE is designed to fit into your revision structure and provide you with the facts and examples you will need while working at home. This book is written for Higher Level, sometimes known as Further Level or 'R' Level (grades D–A*). As you probably are aware, the exam papers at this level are quite demanding.

Revision should not be rushed, so organise a revision timetable well in advance. Check that you know all the facts listed under **Things You Need to Know** in each section. Work through the **How to Do It** questions with the solutions covered, and then check your working carefully against the solutions. When you feel confident to continue, try the **Do It Yourself** questions. You'll find the **Answers** near the end of the book.

You do not have to work through this book in any particular order. Indeed, you should not waste time revising topics that you know how to do, but instead concentrate on those you are not very good at. At this level, it is particularly important that your algebra is good.

The numbering system used in the book makes it easy for you to concentrate on whatever topics you feel you most need to revise. Each topic within a section has a number, which identifies that topic throughout the section. Thus, in Section 1, for example, a brief explanation of powers appears in no. 3 of Things You Need to Know; then exercise 3a, 3b and 3c of How to Do It show you how to answer questions involving powers; and finally you can check how well you understand powers with Do It Yourself exercises 3a, 3b, 3c and 3d.

About a fortnight before the examination, you can try the **Sample Exam Paper** at the end of the book. It is made up of the type of questions you will get in the actual exam, and should take you about two to two-and-a-half hours to do. Remember, you may well be unable to do all the questions. The solutions are given at the end of the paper. If this were a real GCSE exam, you'd need to get about 50 per cent correct for Grade C level, and about 75 per cent correct for grade A level.

In the actual examination, do not spend too long on any one question. You can always go back if you have time at the end.

Try to enjoy your revision. You'll be surprised how this helps. Remember, the more you practise, the better you will cope.

1 | Number Work and Indices

Things You Need to Know

1 **Rounding** – we often need to express a number by rounding it off. Numbers are normally rounded to a certain number of significant figures or a number of decimal places. These figures are generally the figures 1 to 9, but can be the figure 0 in special circumstances. (We don't count the 0 when it is a leading 0 or when it is a trailing 0 – in other words it is counted when it is in the middle of other figures.)

To round to a particular number of significant figures (s.f.) or decimal places (d.p.) we look at the figure after the last required figure – if it is 5 or higher then the last figure is increased by 1, otherwise it is left as it is. For example:

> 674 829 is 674 800 correct to four significant figures
> or 675 000 correct to three significant figures.

Here is an example where the 0 can be a significant figure:

> 7065 is 7070 correct to three significant figures
> or is 7100 correct to two significant figures.
> 4.794 is 4.8 to one decimal place and 4.79 to two decimal places.

2 **Negative numbers** refer to a position below (or to the left of) some zero point. When two signs come together like $2 + (-3)$ consider how the signs affect each other and the outcome. This is summarised in the table:

1st sign	2nd sign	result
+	+	+
+	−	−
−	+	−
−	−	+

So, $2 + (-3)$ becomes $2 - 3$, which is -1.

The same rules apply when we multiply two numbers together. For example:

$-3 \times -6 = +18$ (we would not normally put the $+$ sign in)

'If the two numbers have the same sign, the answer is positive. If the signs are different, the answer is negative'

3 **Powers** or **index numbers** – multiplying a number by itself several times is something that is often done in mathematics. For example:

$$7 \times 7 \times 7 \times 7 \times 7 \times 7 \times 7 \times 7 \times 7 = 7^9$$

The 9 tells how many of the 7s have been multiplied together. The rules for handling this shorthand are fairly straightforward (providing the base number is the same):

$$n^a \times n^b = n^{a+b}$$
$$n^a \div n^b = \frac{n^a}{n^b} = n^{a-b}$$
$$(n^a)^b = n^{a \times b}$$

When the base number is not the same, then the values need to be worked upon to give the same base number. Here is an example:

$$25^4 \times 5^3 = ?$$
$$= (5^2)^4 \times 5^3$$
$$= 5^8 \times 5^3$$
$$= 5^{11}$$

There is one special power and that is 0. Whatever the number to the power of 0 the result is 1. Here is one reason why we consider it to be 1:

$$12^0 \times 12^7 = 12^{0+7} = 12^7$$

So 12^0 has not changed 12^7.

The rules above are easy to follow for whole numbers, but what about negative numbers? Consider:

$$5^{-3} \times 5^3 = ?$$
$$= 5^0 \quad \text{(using the rules)}$$
$$= 1$$

so

$$5^{-3} \times 5^3 = 1$$

thus

$$5^{-3} = \frac{1}{5^3}$$

A number to a negative power means

$$\frac{1}{\text{the number to the positive power}}$$

or it is the **reciprocal**.

What about the fractional roots? Consider

$$(5^{1/2})^2 = 5^1 \text{ or } 5$$

so

$$5^{1/2} = \sqrt{5}$$

Similarly:

$$10^{1/3} = \sqrt[3]{10} \text{ and } 67^{1/4} = \sqrt[4]{67}$$

So, the $\frac{1}{2}$ power means the square root
the $\frac{1}{3}$ power means the cube root
and the $\frac{1}{4}$ power means the fourth root.

Always work everything out in the root sign and *then* find the root. Remember:

$$\sqrt{16+9} \neq \sqrt{16} + \sqrt{9} \text{ (this would give 7)}$$
$$\text{Instead, } \sqrt{16+9} = \sqrt{25}$$
$$= 5$$

4 **Standard form** – some numbers have lots and lots of figures in them, like the number for the speed of light: 299 500 kilometres a second, which is 1 078 200 000 kilometres per hour! Some numbers are very small, like the mass of the electron:

> 0.000 000 000 000 000 000 000 000 000 910 929

To make it easier to write down, put the number down with the decimal place so that the number is between 1 and 10. This has to be multiplied by a power of 10 to re-position the decimal point in the correct place. To do this, count how many figures the decimal point has been moved; this is the power of the ten (with a minus sign if the original number is less than 1). For example,

$$299\,500 = 2.995 \times 10^5$$

$$0.000\,000\,000\,000\,000\,000\,000\,000\,000\,910\,929 = 9.109\,29 \times 10^{-28}$$

How to Do It

1 Use a calculator to find the value of each of the following. Correct your answer to the accuracy asked for.

    (i) 4.3×2.65 (1 d.p.)   (ii) $2.583 \div 0.856$ (2 d.p.)
    (iii) 34.5×62.3 (to nearest 10)   (iv) 3.35×2.28 (to 3 s.f.)

Solution

(i) $4.3 \times 2.65 = 11.395$ (on some calculators)
            $= 11.4$ (to 1 d.p.)
(ii) $2.583 \div 0.856 = 3.017\,5234$ (on some calculators)
               $= 3.02$ (to 2 d.p.)
(iii) $34.5 \times 62.3 = 2149.35$ (on some calculators)
             $= 2150$ (to nearest 10)
(iv) $3.35 \times 2.28 = 7.638$ (on some calculators)
            $= 7.64$ (to 3 s.f.)

2 Evaluate the following:

    (i) -4×3 (ii) -5×-7 (iii) $-48 \div 12$ (iv) $-1 \times -2 \times -3 \times -4 \times -5$

'When you use a calculator, work with as many figures as possible, but when you quote an answer, correct it to two or three decimal places, or to four significant figures, as appropriate'

Solution

(i) $-4 \times 3 = -12$

(ii) $-5 \times -7 = +35$ (or just 35)

(iii) $-48 \div 12 = -4$

(iv) $-1 \times -2 \times -3 \times -4 \times -5 = 2 \times 12 \times -5$ (working out the pairs from left to right)

$$= 24 \times -5$$
$$= -120 \text{ (take care with the signs)}$$

3 a Simplify the following:

(i) $4^2 \times 4^5$ (ii) $5^7 \times 5^{-3}$ (iii) $4^5 \div 4^{-2}$ (iv) $(\tfrac{1}{2})^3 \div (\tfrac{1}{2})^{-6}$

Solution

(i) $4^2 \times 4^5 = (4 \times 4) \times (4 \times 4 \times 4 \times 4 \times 4) = 4^{2+5} = 4^7$

(ii) $5^7 \times 5^{-3} = 5^{7+(-3)} = 5^4$

(iii) $4^5 \div 4^{-2} = 4^{5-(-2)} = 4^{5+2} = 4^7$

(iv) $(\tfrac{1}{2})^3 \div (\tfrac{1}{2})^{-6} = (\tfrac{1}{2})^{3-(-6)} = (\tfrac{1}{2})^9$

(Since $\tfrac{1}{2}$ is 2^{-1}, we could write it as 2^{-9}.)

b What is $\dfrac{3^9}{3^6 \times 3^5}$ as a single power of 3?

Solution

$$\frac{3^9}{3^6 \times 3^5} = \frac{3^9}{3^{6+5}} = \frac{3^9}{3^{11}} = 3^{9-11} = 3^{-2}$$

c Replace the ? by the correct index value:

(i) $9 = 3^?$ (ii) $2^? = 16$ (iii) $100\,000 = 10^?$ (iv) $\tfrac{1}{4} = 2^?$

Solution

(i) $9 = 3^?$ $? = 2$ (because $9 = 3^2$)

(ii) $2^? = 16$ $? = 4$ (because $2^4 = 16$)

(iii) $100\,000 = 10^?$ $? = 5$ (because $100\,000 = 10^5$)

(iv) $\tfrac{1}{4} = 2^?$ $? = -2$ (because $\tfrac{1}{4} = 2^{-2}$)

4 **a** Convert the following to standard form:

(i) 57 000   (ii) 0.000 69   (iii) 34×10^3 (iv) 0.64×10^{-7}

Solution

(i) $57\,000 = 5.7 \times 10^4$ (ii) $0.000\,69 = 6.9 \times 10^{-4}$

(iii) $34 \times 10^3 = 3.4 \times 10 \times 10^3$ (iv) $0.64 \times 10^{-7} = 6.4 \times 10^{-1} \times 10^{-7}$

$\qquad\qquad = 3.4 \times 10^4$ $\qquad\qquad\qquad = 6.4 \times 10^{-8}$

b What are the following in ordinary notation?

(i) 3.5×10^4 (ii) 2.9×10^{-5} (iii) $5.983\,67 \times 10^3$

Solution

(i) $3.5 \times 10^4 = 35\,000$

(ii) $2.9 \times 10^{-5} = 0.000\,029$

(iii) $5.983\,67 \times 10^3 = 5983.67$

c Work out the following, leaving your answer in standard form:

(i) $(1.8 \times 10^3)^2$ (ii) $(4 \times 10^8)^3$ (iii) $(5.1 \times 10^{-6})^3$

Solution

(i) $(1.8 \times 10^3)^2 = 1.8 \times 10^3 \times 1.8 \times 10^3$

$\qquad\qquad\qquad = 3.24 \times 10^6$

(ii) $(4 \times 10^8)^3 = 4 \times 10^8 \times 4 \times 10^8 \times 4 \times 10^8$

$\qquad\qquad\quad = 4^3 \times (10^8)^3$

$\qquad\qquad\quad = 64 \times 10^{24}$

$\qquad\qquad\quad = 6.4 \times 10^{25}$

(iii) $(5.1 \times 10^{-6})^3 = 5.1 \times 10^{-6} \times 5.1 \times 10^{-6} \times 5.1 \times 10^{-6}$

$\qquad\qquad\qquad = 5.1^3 \times (10^{-6})^3$

$\qquad\qquad\qquad = 132.651 \times 10^{-18}$

$\qquad\qquad\qquad = 1.326\,51 \times 10^2 \times 10^{-18}$

$\qquad\qquad\qquad = 1.326\,51 \times 10^{-16}$

Do It Yourself

1 **a** Write each of the following numbers correct to the nearest 100, correct to three significant figures, and correct to two decimal places:

   (i) 9326.686   (ii) 85.513   (iii) 227.245

b Using a calculator find the following and write your answers correct to three significant figures:

   (i) $\sqrt{7}$ (ii) $2\sqrt{11}$ (iii) $\dfrac{5}{9}$ (iv) 3.412^2

2 Work out (or evaluate):

   (i) $-11+7$ (ii) $-8+(-6)$ (iii) $7-(-2)$ (iv) $\dfrac{6}{-3}$

   (v) $(-4)\times(-7)$ (vi) $-21\div3$ (vii) $5(3-(-7))$ (viii) $\dfrac{7\times(-6)}{-3}$

   (ix) $(-6)\times(-4)\times(-10)$ (x) $\dfrac{6\times(-2)-3}{-4}$

3 **a** Simplify: (i) $2^2\times2^3$ (ii) $4^3\times4^4$ (iii) $3^6\div3^4$ (iv) $2^8\div2^2$

   (v) $\dfrac{3^4\times3^5}{3^3}$ (vi) $2^4\times8^3$ (vii) $9^2\times27^5$ (viii) $32^3\div4^4$

b (i) If $310\,000 = 3.1\times10^n$, what is the value of n?
   (ii) What is 4.1×10^{-3} as a decimal?

c Calculate the following, using a calculator only where you need to. Leave your answers as fractions where necessary.

   (i) 5^{-1} (ii) 2^{-3} (iii) 4^0 (iv) $9^{1/2}$ (v) $8^{1/3}$ (vi) $36^{-1/2}$

d Work out: (i) $(6\times10^{-3})\div(4\times10^{-1})$ (ii) $(3\times10^{-4})\times(4\times10^6)$

4 Write the following numbers in standard form:

   (i) 5971   (ii) 78 000   (iii) 0.003 52   (iv) 14 million

14

Number Patterns

Things You Need to Know

1   **Triangular numbers** are those where the number of objects can be set out in a triangle shape – the first (or top) row is one object, the second row is two objects, the third row is three objects and so on.

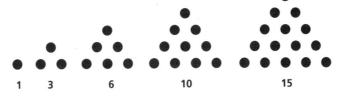

| 1 | 3 | 6 | 10 | 15 |

2   **Square numbers** are the result of squaring a number; also that particular number of objects can be arranged in a square.

$$1^2 = 1 \qquad 2^2 = 4 \qquad 3^2 = 9 \qquad 4^2 = 16 \qquad 5^2 = \ldots \text{ and so on}$$

so the square numbers are

    1   4   9   16   ... and so on

36 is a square number as you can see in the diagram.

3 **Cube numbers** are simply those numbers resulting from cubing the counting numbers.

$$1^3 = 1 \qquad 2^3 = 8 \qquad 3^3 = 27 \qquad 4^3 = 64 \qquad 5^3 = \ldots \text{ and so on}$$

so the cube numbers are

1   8   27   64   . . . and so on

4 It is possible to have a sequence of numbers generated that depend upon a rule that uses previous numbers in the sequence. One such pattern here is called the **Fibonacci series**. In this series any number is the sum of the two before it. However, we must state the first two numbers before we can begin producing the rest of the numbers. If we start with 1 and 1 we get

1   1   2   3   5   8   13   21   34   55   . . . and so on

'We could start the series with any two numbers, but the principle is the same'

5 When meeting a series of numbers, we often need to spot the pattern it contains – in other words, to find the rule which is generating the numbers. One obvious way is to look carefully to see if the numbers are recognisable; for example, are they always odd, or even, or some other special sort of number (e.g. a multiple of 3, say). Failing that, do the numbers differ from each other in a particular way? For example, what are the next two numbers in the following sequence?

1   2   4   7   11   16   22   ?   ?

The answer is 29 and 37. The differences between the neighbouring pairs are

1   2   3   4   5   6   . . .

so the next one is 7 and the one after that is 8.

How to Do It

1 (i) Show that 28 is a triangular number.

(ii) If T_1 means the first triangular number, T_2 the second and T_3 the third triangular number, what is the result of $T_1 + T_2 + T_3$? Is the result a triangular number?

Solution

(i) There are two ways – one is by adding the counting numbers:

$$1+2+3+4+5+6+7 = 28$$

(so it is a triangular number)

The other way is by diagram:

(ii) $T_1 + T_2 + T_3 = 1+3+6 = 10$

10 is the fourth triangular number.

2a Which of the following are square numbers?

(i) 144   (ii) 99   (iii) 49   (iv) 400

Solution

(i) $144 = 12^2$ so it is a square number

(ii) 99 is not a square number ($9^2 = 81$ and $10^2 = 100$)

(iii) $49 = 7^2$ so it is a square number

(iv) $400 = 20^2$ so it is a square number

b Let's represent the nth triangular number as T_n. Find:

(i) $T_1 + T_2$ (ii) $T_6 + T_7$ (iii) $T_9 + T_{10}$

What type of numbers are the results?

Solution

(i) $T_1 + T_2 = 1+3 = 4$

(ii) $T_6 + T_7 = 21+28 = 49$

(iii) $T_9 + T_{10} = 45+55 = 100$

All of the answers are square numbers.

3 Which of the following numbers are cube numbers:

(i) 125   (ii) 343   (iii) 81   (iv) 1000

Solution

(i) $125 = 5^3$ so it is a cube number
(ii) $343 = 7^3$ so it is a cube number
(iii) 81 is not a cube number ($4^3 = 64$ and $5^3 = 125$)
(iv) $1000 = 10^3$ so it is a cube number

4a Consider the following four neighbouring Fibonacci numbers:

8   13   21   34

Multiply the outer pair and mutliply the inner pair; what is the difference between the answers? Try it with another set of four neighbouring Fibonacci numbers – what do you notice?

Solution
The outer pair multiply to give 272 and the inner pair multiply to give 273. The difference is 1.
   Another set: 55   89   144   233.
   The outer pair multiply to give 12 815 and the inner pair multiply to give 12 816. The difference is 1.

b What are the next five terms in a Fibonacci type sequence that starts with 1 and 3?

Solution

1   3   4   7   11   18   29

5a If a rule for generating the nth number in a series is $2n-1$ what is the product of the third and fifth terms?

Solution
'Product' means the answer you get from multiplying the numbers together.

The third term $= 2(3)-1 = 5$
The fifth term $= 2(5)-1 = 9$
The product $= 9 \times 5 = 45$

b Draw the next two patterns in the following two sequences:

(i)

(ii)

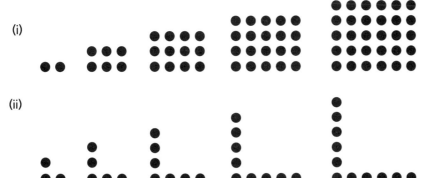

Solution

(i)

(ii)

c What is the formula for each of the patterns in (a) above?

Solution

(i) The numbers go:

        2   6   12   20   30

There is no obvious pattern here, so look at the rectangles. They are

        1×2 2×3 3×4 4×5 5×6

so the formula is $n(n+1)$.

(ii) The numbers go:

        3   5   7   9   11   (the odd numbers)

It is not so easy to state the formula from this, so look at the shape. The arms of the L shape each have n dots plus the corner one, so the formula is $2n+1$.

d Write down the first five terms of the sequences for each of the following rules:

  (i) Start with 3, then keep adding 4.
  (ii) Start with 1, then keep on doubling and add 1.
  (iii) Start with 1, then keep on adding 1 and doubling.

Solution

(i) 3   7   11   15   19
(ii) 1   3   7   15   31
(iii) 1   4   10   22   46

e One way of solving an equation is **trial and improvement** – making a guess and then refining the guess, repeating this until the answer is accurate enough. Consider:

$$x^2 - 5x - 3 = 0$$

Rearranged this can become:

$$x^2 = 5x + 3$$

Dividing both sides by x gives:

$$x = 5 + \frac{3}{x}$$

If we put our 'guess' into the right-hand side of the equation, it will give a new value for x; if this agrees accurately enough with our guess, we have the answer. Use $x = 3$ as the first 'guess' and find a solution of the equation correct to 2 decimal places.

Solution
If $x_1 = 3$ (using the '1' to mean the first guess) then

$$x_2 = 5 + \tfrac{3}{3}$$
$$x_2 = 6$$

If $x_2 = 6$ then

$$x_3 = 5 + \tfrac{3}{6}$$
$$x_3 = 5.5$$

If $x_3 = 5.5$ then

$$x_4 = 5 + \tfrac{3}{5.5}$$
$$x_4 = 5.455 \text{ (corr. to 3 d.p.)}$$

If $x_4 = 5.4545$ then

$$x_5 = 5 + \frac{3}{5.455}$$
$$x_5 = 5.550 \text{ (corr. to 3 d.p.)}$$

If $x_5 = 5.5500$ then

$$x_6 = 5 + \frac{3}{5.550}$$
$$x_6 = 5.541 \text{ (corr. to 3 d.p.)}$$

So

$$x_7 = 5 + \frac{3}{5.451}$$
$$x_7 = 5.541 \text{ (corr. to 3 d.p.)}$$

Thus, to 2 decimal places

$$x = 5.54$$

Do It Yourself

1 Using the first six triangular numbers write down three that are:
   (i) prime numbers;
   (ii) multiples of 5;
   (iii) not multiples of 3.

2 a Extend the following number pattern to find 65^2 and 95^2:

$$5^2 = 0 \times 10 + 25 = 25$$
$$15^2 = 10 \times 20 + 25 = 225$$
$$25^2 = 20 \times 30 + 25 = 625$$

b Draw a square of dots that shows the square of 6. Divide it into two triangles of dots using a diagonal. What two triangular numbers are they? Now use this idea to show that any square is made up of two triangular numbers.

3 Since $4^3 = 64$ and $8^2 = 64$, then 64 is both a cube number and a square number. Find the next cube number that is also a square number.

4 **a** If a b c represent three neighbouring terms in the Fibonacci series, find

$a \times c$ and b^2

What do you notice about the two answers?

b The nth term in a series is given by

$4n + 5$

Find the first 8 terms of the series.
Which of these terms are square numbers?

5 **a** Write down the next two terms in each of the following sequences:

(i) 3   6   9   12   (ii) 4   7   10   13
(iii) 5   10   15   (iv) 20   17   14   11

b Using your calculator work out the values of each of the following terms:

$$\frac{1}{2} \quad \frac{1+3}{2+4} \quad \frac{1+3+5}{2+4+6} \quad \frac{1+3+5+7}{2+4+6+8} \quad \frac{1+3+5+7+9}{2+4+6+8+10}$$

What do you think is a likely value for:

$$\frac{1+3+5+7+9+ \ldots +199}{2+4+6+8+ \ldots +200}$$

Try to give a reason for your answer.

c Show that the equation

$$x^3 - 2x - 5 = 0$$

can be rearranged as:

$$x = \sqrt{2 + \frac{5}{x}}$$

Starting with the value of x as 2, use this rearrangement to find a value of x correct to 2 decimal places.

Fractions

3

Things You Need to Know

1 **Fractions** are a way of saying how much compared to some whole amount. They are written as

$$\frac{\text{numerator}}{\text{denominator}}$$

The fractions $\frac{1}{4}$ and $\frac{2}{8}$ are **equivalent fractions** because they are equal.

A fraction in which the numerator is larger than the denominator is known as an **improper fraction**. $\frac{5}{4}$ is an improper fraction. It is the same as $1\frac{1}{4}$ which is known as a **mixed number**.

A number that can be expressed as a fraction of two integers (whole numbers) is known as a **rational number**. A number that cannot be expressed in this way is an **irrational number**.

2 **Adding** and **subtracting** fractions is easy to do *if* you remember to convert the fractions so they all have the same denominator.

$$\frac{2}{3}+\frac{1}{4} = \frac{8}{12}+\frac{3}{12}$$ (12 is the smallest number divisible by 3 and 4, known as the **lowest common multiple**, or **LCM**)

$$= \frac{11}{12}$$ (sometimes we can cancel this down – but not here)

3 **Multiplying** fractions is simply a matter of multiplying the numerators and multiplying the denominators and then cancelling (if possible).

$$\tfrac{3}{4} \times \tfrac{2}{5} = \tfrac{6}{20} = \tfrac{3}{10}$$

'Remember: dividing by $\tfrac{1}{2}$ is the same as multiplying by 2'

4 **Dividing** fractions is done by turning the dividing fraction upside down and then multiplying.

$$\tfrac{4}{5} \div \tfrac{2}{3} = \tfrac{4}{5} \times \tfrac{3}{2} = \tfrac{12}{10} = \tfrac{6}{5} = 1\tfrac{1}{5}$$

5 When you are using fractions, take care. Read the question carefully. For example, is it asking what fraction has been taken or what fraction is left? If $\tfrac{2}{5}$ has been taken then it means that $\tfrac{3}{5}$ is left behind.

How to Do It

1 **a** Jim's pocket money is £5.00 per week. If he spends $\tfrac{1}{5}$ of it at the tuck shop, spends $\tfrac{3}{4}$ of it on going out, and saves the rest, how much is he actually saving each week?

Solution
$\tfrac{1}{5}$ of £5.00 is £1, and $\tfrac{3}{4}$ of £5.00 is £3.75. So Jim is saving £0.25.

b State whether the following numbers are rational or irrational.
(i) 3 (ii) $\sqrt{16}$ (iii) 3.73 (iv) $\sqrt{3}$

Solution
(i) Rational ($\tfrac{3}{1}$) (ii) Rational (4 or -4) (iii) Rational ($\tfrac{373}{100}$)
(iv) Irrational: $\sqrt{3}$ cannot be expressed exactly as a fraction.

2 Find the value of $2\tfrac{1}{3} - 3\tfrac{1}{2} + 1\tfrac{1}{5}$.

Solution

$$2\tfrac{1}{3} - 3\tfrac{1}{2} + 1\tfrac{1}{5} = \tfrac{7}{3} - \tfrac{7}{2} + \tfrac{6}{5}$$

The lowest common multiple of 3, 2 and 5 is 30:

$$\tfrac{7}{3} - \tfrac{7}{2} + \tfrac{6}{5} = \tfrac{70}{30} - \tfrac{7 \times 15}{30} + \tfrac{6 \times 6}{30} = \tfrac{70 - 105 + 36}{30} = \tfrac{1}{30}$$

3 Work out the following:

$$\text{(i) } \tfrac{3}{8} \times \tfrac{2}{7} \qquad \text{(ii) } \tfrac{4}{9} \times 1\tfrac{1}{3} \qquad \text{(iii) } 2\tfrac{5}{8} \times 1\tfrac{1}{3}$$

Solution

(i) $\tfrac{3}{8} \times \tfrac{2}{7} = \tfrac{6}{56} = \tfrac{3}{28}$

(ii) $\tfrac{4}{9} \times 1\tfrac{1}{3} = \tfrac{4}{9} \times \tfrac{4}{3} = \tfrac{16}{27}$ (no cancelling possible)

(iii) $2\tfrac{5}{8} \times 1\tfrac{1}{3} = \tfrac{21}{8} \times \tfrac{4}{3}$
$$= \tfrac{7 \times 1}{2 \times 1} = \tfrac{7}{2} = 3\tfrac{1}{2}$$

4 Work out the following:

$$\text{(i) } \tfrac{5}{6} \div \tfrac{1}{3} \qquad \text{(ii) } 1\tfrac{1}{5} \div \tfrac{7}{10} \qquad \text{(iii) } 2\tfrac{2}{3} \div 3\tfrac{5}{9}$$

Solution

(i) $\tfrac{5}{6} \div \tfrac{1}{3} = \tfrac{5}{6} \times \tfrac{3}{1}$
$$= \tfrac{5 \times 1}{2 \times 1} = \tfrac{5}{2} = 2\tfrac{1}{2}$$

(ii) $1\tfrac{1}{5} \div \tfrac{7}{10} = \tfrac{6}{5} \div \tfrac{7}{10} = \tfrac{6}{5} \times \tfrac{10}{7}$
$$= \tfrac{6 \times 2}{1 \times 7} = \tfrac{12}{7} = 1\tfrac{5}{7}$$

(iii) $2\tfrac{2}{3} \div 3\tfrac{5}{9} = \tfrac{8}{3} \div \tfrac{32}{9} = \tfrac{8}{3} \times \tfrac{9}{32}$
$$= \tfrac{1 \times 3}{1 \times 4} = \tfrac{3}{4}$$

5a Alan, Brenda and Chris started a joint business. In the first year their profits were £18 000. Alan received $\tfrac{2}{5}$ of the profit, Brenda received $\tfrac{1}{3}$ and Chris received the rest. How much did each receive?

Alan: $\tfrac{2}{5}$ of £18 000 = £$\tfrac{36\,000}{5}$ = £7200
Brenda: $\tfrac{1}{3}$ of £18 000 = £$\tfrac{18\,000}{3}$ = £6000
Chris: £18 000 − (£7200 + £6000) = £4800

b What is the simplest fraction for the recurring decimal 0.272 727 2727?

Solution

$$y = 0.272\,727\,2727\ldots$$
$$100y = 27.272\,727\,2727\ldots$$

Subtract y:

$$99y = 27$$
$$y = \tfrac{27}{99}$$
$$y = \tfrac{3}{11}$$

'When an answer is reached, you can sometimes cancel it down. Even though it is not always possible, you should check'

Do It Yourself

1 **a** For each of the shapes below, write down the fraction shaded and the fraction unshaded – both in their simplest form:

(i)   (ii)   (iii)   (iv)

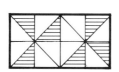 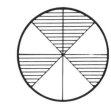

b Where possible rewrite the following fractions in their simplest form:

$$\frac{6}{8} \quad \frac{9}{27} \quad \frac{6}{20} \quad \frac{4}{18} \quad \frac{14}{35} \quad \frac{75}{150}$$

c A tool kit has spanners in the following sizes:

$$\frac{5}{8} \quad \frac{1}{2} \quad \frac{1}{8} \quad \frac{9}{16} \quad \frac{3}{8} \quad \frac{1}{4} \quad \frac{5}{16} \quad \frac{7}{8} \quad \frac{7}{16} \quad \frac{3}{4} \quad \frac{11}{16}$$

Arrange them in order of size.

2 Work out the following:

(i) $\frac{2}{3} + \frac{1}{5}$ (ii) $\frac{3}{4} + \frac{1}{10}$ (iii) $\frac{3}{5} - \frac{1}{7}$ (iv) $\frac{4}{9} - \frac{1}{6}$

3 Work out:

(i) $\frac{3}{8} \times \frac{4}{9}$ (ii) $\frac{2}{3} \times \frac{5}{6}$

4 Work out:

(i) $\frac{5}{7} \div \frac{3}{14}$ (ii) $\frac{5}{8} \div \frac{4}{5}$

5 Find the simplest fraction for

(i) 0.545 454 54 . . .

(ii) 0.111 111 . . .

Percentages and Ratios

Things You Need to Know

1 **Percentage** means 'out of 100', so if you achieved a mark of 80 out of a possible 100 for an examination your result would be 80%; it can also be thought of as a fraction with 100 as the denominator and the percentage figure as the numerator.

2 **Ratio** is a comparison of sizes. For example, the ratio 3 : 1 means that there is three times as much of one quantity as the other.

How to Do It

1 a If you got 15 out of 20 for one test and 18 out of 25 for another, which is the better performance?

Solution

$$\frac{15}{20} = \frac{15}{20} \times 100\%$$

$$= \frac{15}{1} \times 5\% \quad \text{(cancelling by 20)}$$

$$= 75\%$$

$$\frac{18}{25} = \frac{18}{25} \times 100\%$$

$$= \frac{18}{1} \times 4\% \quad \text{(cancelling by 25)}$$

$$= 72\%$$

So we can see that 15 out of 20 is better than 18 out of 25.

A different way of writing a percentage is as a decimal:

$$23\% = \frac{23}{100} = 0.23$$

Remember, for a percentage to mean anything we have to know what 100% means – in other words it has to be a percentage of something (for example, a price, maximum marks in an examination or a whole cake).

b What percentage is 150 mm of 1 m?

Solution

If you have to find what percentage something is of something else, they have to be in the same units.

$$1\,m = 1000\,mm$$

So 150 mm is

$$\frac{150}{1000} \times 100\% = \frac{150}{10} \times 1\% = 15\%$$

The most common example of the use of percentages is with Value Added Tax (VAT), a form of sales tax. At the time of writing, VAT is $17\frac{1}{2}\%$. If you are given the price without VAT, finding the price with it is simply a matter of calculating 117.5% of the price.

If you have the price with VAT, finding the price without it is a little more tricky. Remember that the price with VAT is 117.5% and you need to find what 100% is. Therefore, you divide the price with VAT by 117.5 and multiply by 100 – using a calculator makes this very easy to do!

c Sam's vegetable garden is a rectangular plot 25 m long and 15 m wide. He increases the length by 15% and decreases the width by 5%. What is the change in area in square metres? Also express this as a percentage of the original area.

Solution
Method 1

New length = 100% + 15% of the old length
= 115% × 25 m
= 28.75 m

New width = 100% − 5% of the old width
= 95% × 15 m
= 14.25 m

Old area = 25 m × 15 m
= 375 m²

New area = 28.75 m × 14.25 m
= 409.7 m²   (to 1 d.p.)

Change in area = 34.7 m²

As a percentage of the original area,

$$\text{Change in area} = \frac{34.7}{375} \times 100\%$$
$$= 9.3\%   \text{(to 1 d.p.)}$$

'Make sure that you can use the % button on your calculator'

The calculator is useful for this type of computation. For example, to work out 95% of 15 metres, press the following keys:

| 9 | 5 | % | × | 1 | 5 | = |

Method 2

As new length is 115% of old length
and new width is 95% of old width
then new area is 115% × 95% of old area

$$= 1.15 \times 0.95 \text{ of old area}$$
$$= 1.0925 \text{ of old area}$$
$$\text{or } 109.25\% \text{ of old area}$$

from which we see that new area is 9.25% larger than old area.

d The value of Sharon's car decreases by 20% each year. If her car was originally worth £10 000, how much will it be worth after 5 years?

Solution

Method 1

Value at start of year 1 = £10 000	Depreciation = 20% of £10 000 = £2000
Value at start of year 2 = £8000	Depreciation = 20% of £8000 = £1600
Value at start of year 3 = £6400	Depreciation = 20% of £6400 = £1280
Value at start of year 4 = £5120	Depreciation = 20% of £5120 = £1024
Value at start of year 5 = £4096	Depreciation = 20% of £4096 = £819.20
Value at end of year 5 = £3276.80	

Method 2

As the loss in value is 20% of the original, then the new value is 80% of the original value.

Value at start of year 1	= £10 000	
Value at start of year 2 (or end of year 1)	= 80% of £10 000	= £8000
Value at start of year 3 (or end of year 2)	= 80% of £8000	= £6400
Value at start of year 4 (or end of year 3)	= 80% of £6400	= £5120
Value at start of year 5 (or end of year 4)	= 80% of £5120	= £4096
Value at start of year 5	= 80% of £4096	= £3276.80

e A dealer in antiques always makes a profit of 30% on her sales. She buys a desk for £180; what must be her selling price?

Solution

There are two possible ways to solve this – find the profit and add on to the selling price or use the fact that the selling price is 130% of the buying price.

Method 1

Profit = 30% of £180 = £54

So selling price is

£180 + £54 = £234

Method 2

Selling price = 130% of £180 = £234

f Janet takes two examinations, each out of 100 marks. In the first she got 72%, but unfortunately in the second she lost half as many marks again as she did in the first examination. What is her overall percentage mark for the two examinations?

Solution

Score in first examination = 72%

So she lost 28%. In the second examination she lost half as many again:

28% + 14% = 42%

So her mark in the second examination was

58%   (100% − 42%)

Janet scored 130 (72 + 58) in the two examinations, out of a possible 200:

$$\frac{130}{200} \times 100\% = 65\%$$

2

a Three children divide a bag of sweets up in the ratio of $3:4:5$. If there are 48 sweets in the bag, how many sweets does each child get?

Solution

The total number of parts the bag is divided up into is $3+4+5 = 12$. As there are 48 sweets that means that each part is 4 sweets. So

The first child gets 3 parts or 12 sweets.
The second child gets 4 parts or 16 sweets.
The third child gets 5 parts or 20 sweets.

You might also notice that we could have written the ratio as $12:16:20$. However, it is common practice to use the smallest set of numbers. So in this case we divide by 4 to obtain $3:4:5$.

'At the end it is sensible to check that the total number of sweets is still 48!'

b A health club has men and women members in the ratio $4:5$. The club has 196 men; how many members does it have?

Solution

Men : women $= 4:5$ (a total of 9 parts)

So 4 parts represent 196 members, hence 1 part is 49 members. Therefore the complete membership (the 9 parts) is

$9 \times 49 = 441$ members

c A piece of wood is to be cut up into the ratio $2:3:5$. What fraction of the original length is the smallest part?

Solution

Total of the parts $= 10$

So the fraction of length for the smallest part is

$$\frac{2}{10} = \frac{1}{5}$$

Do It Yourself

1

a In a sale prices are reduced by 15%. How much does Anne pay for a coat marked at £55.00?

b Ace Bargain Company allow a $3\frac{1}{2}$% discount for a cash sale. What is the cash price of an article marked at £23.00?

c Currently VAT is 17.5%. Find the full price (to the nearest penny) of:

    (i) a sofa-bed   £199 + VAT

    (ii) a CD player   £90 + VAT

    (iii) a badminton racquet   £31.50 + VAT

d If VAT is charged at 17.5%, find the price to the nearest penny of the following items before VAT was added to their price:

    (i) a CD collection costing £24.99

    (ii) a game computer costing £39.99

    (iii) a shirt costing £25.00

    (iv) a gold lace dress costing £55.00

e Choudra runs the 100 m race in her school sports day in 13.2 seconds. The length of the track is measured to the nearest metre and the time is measured to the nearest tenth of a second.

    (i) What is the maximum distance the track could be?

    (ii) What is the minimum distance the track could be?

    (iii) What is the maximum time Choudra could have taken to run the race and still record 13.2 seconds?

    (iv) What is the minimum time Choudra could have taken to run the race and still record 13.2 seconds?

Using the maximum distance and minimum time, find Choudra's maximum possible average speed over the 100 m in metres per second.

f A dealer bought a car for £5000 and sold it at a profit of 20%. The buyer later sold it back to the dealer for 20% less than he paid for it. How much did the buyer get when he resold the car?

2 **a**   (i) Divide £45 in the ratio 2 : 3.   (ii) Divide 42 m in the ratio 4 : 3.

          (iii) Divide 63 kg in the ratio 2 : 3 : 4.

b 'No Mess', the new wonder washing powder, has three main ingredients known as Spotto, Marko and Soapo, in the ratio 4 : 2 : 1. In a box containing 2.8 kg of 'No Mess', how much Marko is there?

'Work out the total number of parts by adding the numbers in the ratio'

5 | Practical Maths

Things You Need to Know

1 'Interest' is the term used to describe either the extra money paid when you borrow money, or the extra money earned by your money in the building society. It is usually expressed as a percentage of the original amount (e.g. 6%). Interest is usually paid (or charged) yearly and this is termed 'per annum' (p.a.).

2 In the case of **simple interest** the interest is worked out each year on the money and this is then kept separate.

3 In the case of **compound interest** the interest gets added to the current amount and so your interest increases each year.

How to Do It

1 Ian invests £500 for one year and receives £550 at the end of the year. What is the annual rate of interest?

Solution

Interest earned $= £550 - £500 = £50$

Interest rate $= \dfrac{50}{500} \times 100 = 10\%$ per annum

2 a If Tracy borrows £250 for 3 years at 8% per annum simple interest, how much does she have to pay back?

Solution

Each year the interest is

$£250 \times 8\% = £20$

But she borrows it for 3 years so the total interest is

$3 \times £20 = £60$

So she has to pay back

$£250 + £60 = £310$

b £200 is invested at 7% p.a. simple interest. How much does it amount to after 3 years?

Solution

Interest each year $= 7\% \times £200 = £14.00$
So simple interest for 3 years is $3 \times £14.00 = £42.00$
Hence amount $= £242$.

c Denise invests £1000 at $6\frac{1}{2}\%$ p.a. simple interest. When she withdraws all her money it has grown to £1260. For how many years did she leave it invested?

Solution

Interest earned each year $= 6\frac{1}{2}\% \times £1000 = £65$

Interest earned $= £1260 - £1000 = £260$

Number of years $= \dfrac{260}{65} = 4$ years

3 **a** If Tracy borrows £250 for 3 years at 8% per annum compound interest, how much does she have to pay back now?

Solution

At the start of year 1 she borrows £250

Interest for year 1 $= £250 \times 8\% = £20$

At the end of year 1 she owes $£250 + £20 = £270$

At the start of year 2 she owes £270

Interest for year 2 $= £270 \times 8\% = £21.60$

At the end of year 2 she owes $£270 + £21.60 = £291.60$

At the start of year 3 she owes £291.60

Interest for year 3 $= £291.60 \times 8\% = £23.33$ (to the nearest penny)

At the end of year 3 she owes £314.93

So she has to pay back £314.93 (nearly £5.00 more than if it were simple interest).

b £400 is left in the Maths County Building Society where it earns 8% compound interest p.a. How many complete years must it be left for it to become over £500?

Solution
Method 1

At the start of year 1 the amount is £400

Interest earned in year 1 $= 8\% \times £400 = £32$

At the start of year 2 the amount is £432

Interest earned in year 2 $= 8\% \times £432 = £34.56$

'In real life the interest rate does not stay the same – it can go up (bad news for borrowers) or down (bad news for lenders)'

At the start of year 3 the amount is £466.56
Interest earned in year 3 = 8% × £466.56 = £37.32

At the start of year 4 the amount is £503.88

So it takes 3 years for it to amount to over £500.

Method 2
As the interest is 8%, this means that the amount at the end of a year is 108% of what it was at the beginning, or 1.08 of what it was at the beginning. So

after Year 1 it is 1.08 × 400
after Year 2 it is 1.08 × (1.08 × 400)
after Year 3 it is 1.08 × [1.08 × (1.08 × 400)] or $1.08^3 × 400$
Using a calculator to work this out gives £503.88.

As a general rule, add the interest rate to 100, convert to a percentage, raise to the power of the number of years and then multiply by the principal (original amount).

Do It Yourself

1 In order to borrow £18 000 from the Bricklayers Building Society the repayments are £12.50 per calendar month per £1000 borrowed for 10 years.
 (i) Calculate the monthly payment.
(ii) How much interest is paid over the 10 years?

2 **a** Find the simple interest paid on £480 for 4 years at 5% per annum.

 b John receives a present of £80 and decides to put it into the bank, where it earns simple interest at a rate of 11% per annum. How many years must he leave it in the bank to receive £44 interest?

3 Harry has £400 to invest for a period of 3 years. He could invest it at $12\frac{1}{2}$% p.a. simple interest or 10% p.a. compound interest. Which is the better investment and by how much is it better?

6 Scale, Maps and Bearings

Things You Need to Know

1 The **scale** tells us how much bigger (or smaller) the real thing is compared to the scaled object. It is used mainly for models and maps. For example:

 1:30   *or*   1 to 30   *or* $\frac{1}{30}$ *or*   1 cm represents 30 cm

Since a map often covers a large area, the scale is often quite small. For instance, some Ordnance Survey maps have a scale of 1:50 000 – on a map like this a house is generally a small dot.

2 How does the scale affect the area on the model or map? Consider a square of side 1 unit which is enlarged by a factor of 5. Each side becomes five times longer, so the new square is 5 units by 5 units and has an area of 25 units² compared to the original area of 1 unit². Therefore, the **area factor** is the *square* of the **scale factor**.

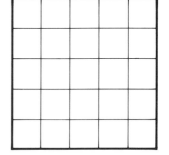

Scale factor is 5, so area factor is 25 (ie. the large square is 25 times the area of the small square)

3 For volume, the three lengths are each changed by the scale factor – so a scale factor of 3 will increase all measurements to three times their value, hence the volume will be 3 × 3 × 3 more than it was. The **volume factor** is therefore the *cube* of the scale factor.

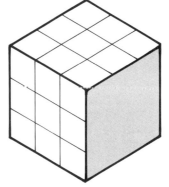

A scale of 3 gives a volume factor of 27

4 With maps we want to be able to find the direction or **bearing** of one point from another. The bearing is always given as a three-figure number that describes the angle that has to be turned through if you face north and turn *clockwise* to face the required direction. For example:

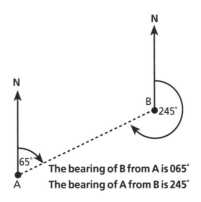

The bearing of B from A is 065°
The bearing of A from B is 245°

'The bearings of opposite directions differ by 180°'

How to Do It

1 a The distance between two towns is 5.2 km, and on the map it is 20.8 cm. What is the scale of the map? Give your answer both in terms of centimetres and kilometres and also as a ratio.

Solution
20.8 cm represents 5.2 km so 1 cm represents

$$\frac{5.2}{20.8} \text{km} = 0.25 \text{km}$$

1 cm represents

$$0.25 \times 1000 \times 100 \text{ cm} = 25\,000 \text{ cm}$$

So the scale is 1 : 25 000.

'Scale is simply the ratio of the length on a model to the length on the real thing'

b A plan of a rectangular room has a scale of 1 : 8. The room is 12 ft by 16 ft. What is its size on the plan?

Solution

The scale of 1 : 8 means that 1 ft represents 8 ft, or $\frac{1}{8}$ ft represents 1 ft. So 12 ft is represented by

$$12 \times \tfrac{1}{8}\,\text{ft} = 1.5\,\text{ft}$$

and 16 ft is represented by

$$16 \times \tfrac{1}{8}\,\text{ft} = 2\,\text{ft}$$

So the room dimensions on the plan are 2 ft × 1.5 ft (or 24 in × 18 in).

2 At FastFilm Developers the cost of a photograph depends upon the area of the photograph. If you have a 4 × 5 inch photograph done, it costs 30p. How much will it cost for an 8 × 10 inch photograph?

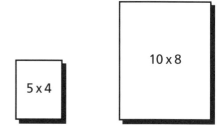

The scale factor is 2

Area factor = 2^2 = 4

Solution

So the price is 4 × 30p = 120p = £1.20.

3 Henry builds a model plane to a scale of 1 : 60. He calculates the volume of the fuselage as 70 cm³. What is the volume of the real fuselage?

Solution

The scale is 1 : 60 :

> 1 cm on the model is 60 cm on the real plane
> 1 cm² on the model is 60 × 60 cm² on the real plane
> 1 cm³ on the model is 60 × 60 × 60 cm³ on the real plane

which is

$$\frac{60 \times 60 \times 60}{100 \times 100 \times 100}\,\text{m}^3 = 0.216\,\text{m}^3$$

So 70 cm³ represents 70 × 0.216 m³ = 15.12 m³

4 Explorers in the Sahara desert leave their base camp. They travel north for 30 km, then 048° for 15 km and finally 30 km on a bearing of 103°. How far are they from base camp, and what is its bearing? (Use a scale of 1 cm to 10 km.)

Solution

From an accurate scale drawing you get:

Distance from base camp = 51 km on a bearing of 231°.

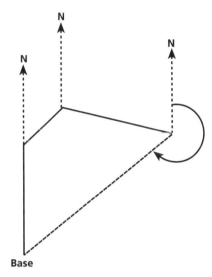

Base

Do It Yourself

1 A coastguard on a cliff top 50 m high sees a boat out at sea at an angle of depression of 10°. By doing a scale drawing, find how far the boat is from the foot of the cliffs – assume that the cliff face is vertical.

'An angle of depression is the angle below a horizontal line'

2 The scale of a map is 1 : 10 000. On the map the area of a woodland is 5 cm². What is the area of the woodland in m²?

3 A model of a room has a scale of 2 cm to 0.25 m. The height of the model is 24 cm, its floor area is 700 cm² and its volume is 16 800 cm³. Find the height, the floor area and the volume of the room.

4 A group of hikers walk 100 m on a bearing of 080° and then 200 m on a bearing of 150°. Draw an accurate scale drawing of the route. By taking measurements from your scale drawing find out how far they have to go to return directly to their starting point and the bearing along which they must travel.

'It is easier to do your scale drawing on graph paper'

7 | Units

'The metric tonne is not quite the same as the imperial ton'

Things You Need to Know

1 The metric system uses the gram (g) as the basic unit of mass, or weight. In the metric system the main weights are:

$$1\,g = 1000 \text{ milligrams (mg)}$$
$$1000\,g = 1 \text{ kilogram (kg)}$$
$$1000\,kg = 1 \text{ tonne (t)}$$

1 kg is about 2.2 lb in the imperial system.
1 lb in the imperial system is about 450 g.

2 The main unit for length in the metric system is the metre (m). It is related to other lengths as follows:

$$1\,m = 1000 \text{ millimetres (mm)}$$
$$1000\,m = 1 \text{ kilometre (km)}$$
$$1\,m = 100 \text{ cm}$$
$$1\,cm = 10 \text{ mm}$$

1 inch in the imperial system is a little over 2.5 cm (or 25 mm).
1 ft in the imperial system is about 30 cm (or 300 mm).
1 m is just a little under 40 inches in the imperial system.

3 The litre (l) is the unit of capacity in the metric system:

> 1 litre = 100 centilitres (cl)
> 1 litre = 1000 millilitres (ml)
> 1 cl = 10 ml

1 litre is a little over $1\frac{3}{4}$ pints in the imperial system.

How to Do It

1 A 10 kg ingot of an alloy has a volume of 2000 cm³ and is going to be made into identical cylinders each of weight 50 g and cross-sectional area of 2 cm². How long will each cylinder be?

Solution
First, find out how many cylinders we should get:

$$\text{Number of cylinders} = \frac{10\,\text{kg}}{50\,\text{g}} = \frac{10 \times 1000\,\text{g}}{50\,\text{g}}$$
$$= 200$$

so

$$\text{Volume of cylinders} = \frac{1}{200} \text{ of ingot volume}$$
$$= \frac{1}{200} \times 2000\,\text{cm}^3$$
$$= 10\,\text{cm}^3$$

that is

$$\text{Volume of cylinder} = \text{area of cross-section} \times \text{height}$$
$$10\,\text{cm}^3 = 2\,\text{cm}^2 \times \text{height}$$
$$\text{Height} = 5\,\text{cm}$$

2 A ream of paper (500 sheets) is 6 cm thick. Find the thickness of one sheet of paper in millimetres.

Solution
500 sheets are 6 cm thick so one sheet is

$$\frac{6}{500} \text{ cm thick} = \frac{6 \times 10}{500} \text{ mm}$$
$$= 0.12 \text{ mm}$$

3 How many 25 ml doses can you get from a bottle of cough medicine which contain 1.7 litres?

Solution

$$\text{Number of doses} = \frac{1.7 \text{ litres}}{25 \text{ ml}} = \frac{1.7 \times 1000 \text{ ml}}{25 \text{ ml}}$$
$$= 68$$

Do It Yourself

1 a Change to kilograms:

    (i) 7431 g   (ii) 376 100 mg   (iii) 4.5 t

b A security firm delivers £100 worth of 1 pence pieces to a supermarket. Calculate the weight of these coins, in kilograms, if each coin weighs 3.45 g

c Write in order of size, smallest first:

    70 g   0.7 kg   700 mg   0.7 mg

d Twenty-four tins of meat are packed into a carton and the total weight is 16 kg. If the carton alone weighs 400 g, calculate the weight of one tin of meat.

e A caterer uses 400 g of potatoes per day for each person. Find the cost of providing for 55 people for 5 days with the potatoes costing 27p per kilogram.

'The precise scientific term is 'mass' but for everyday most people use the word 'weight''

2 **a** Convert to millimetres:

    (i) 4.6 cm   (ii) 7.9 cm   (iii) 9.1 m   (iv) 31.2 m

b Convert to centimetres:

    (i) 5 m   (ii) 9.2 m   (iii) 740 mm   (iv) 6431 mm

c Convert to kilometres:

    (i) 800 m   (ii) 400 cm   (iii) 650 mm   (iv) 21 m

d A ream of paper (500 sheets) weighs 3 kg. What is the weight, in grams, of one sheet? If the pile is 7 cm thick, what is the thickness of one sheet in millimetres?

3 Cough mixture is sold in bottles containing 5 fl. oz. If 1 fl. oz = 28.41 ml, work out to the nearest centilitre the amount that should be put on the bottle label.

8 | Statistics and Probability

Things You Need to Know

1 In mathematics the word 'average' simply means a typical value that represents the set of values. There are three main types of average – the **mean**, the **mode** and the **median**.

$$\text{mean} = \frac{\text{total of the values in the list}}{\text{number of values in the list}}$$

The **median** is the middle value when the values are arranged in order (or half-way between the middle two values).

The **mode** is the value that occurs the most often.

Even if different sets of values have the same mean value, the values may be spread out around the mean differently. There are two ways of measuring the spread: the **range**, which is the difference between the largest and smallest of the values; and the **standard deviation**, which is the result of a calculation based upon how far each of the values is from the mean value.

To find the standard deviation, first find the difference from the mean for each of the values, and then square it; next, total the squares and divide by the number of values; and, finally, find the square root of this. The smaller the figure, the less spread out are the values from the mean value, and vice-versa.

2 If there is a lot of data, it is best summarised in a **frequency table**, which tells us how many times each value has occurred. Sometimes even this is not very useful, particularly if the range of values is quite large and there are possible values that are not used. In this case we group the values in **class intervals**, and produce a **grouped frequency table**. For example, here is a list of marks 50 pupils received in a science examination. For these data it makes sense to group the values as shown in the following grouped frequency table.

```
80  93  63  74  51  60  61  54  69  54
51  44  33  70  40  30  55  57  59  55
 4  51  46  47  56  58  62  33  45  48
37  56  39  51  14  43  47  58  39  42
66  63  65  71  23  26  81  65  77  68
```

Mark group	Mid-value	Frequency	Freq. × mid-value
0–9	4.5	1	4.5
10–19	14.5	1	14.5
20–29	24.5	2	49
30–39	34.5	6	207
40–49	44.5	9	400.5
50–59	55.5	14	777
60–69	65.5	10	655
70–79	75.5	4	302
80–89	85.5	2	171
90–99	95.5	1	95.5
		50	2676

The table provides a useful way to estimate the mean, using the mid-value of each group, and assuming that this is the value of each value in that group. (Some will be higher and some lower, but it should more or less even out.) To estimate the **mean**, you divide the total of the mid-values by the number of entries. So, in our example,

$$\text{mean} = \frac{\text{total of mid-values}}{\text{number of entries}} = \frac{2676}{50} = 53.52$$

(Compare this figure with the mean obtained using the individual figures: 52.68.)

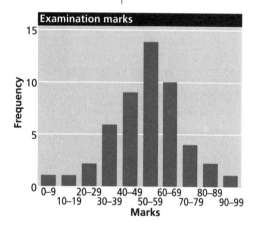

3 A **frequency diagram** is used to represent a frequency table; it has frequency on the vertical axis. When you draw a frequency diagram don't forget to label the axes and put a title. The frequency diagram given here shows the data from the above example.

The grouped frequency table can be made into a cumulative frequency table, by the addition of another column. This provides a running total of the frequency. In the preceding chart, the cumulative frequency column would read 1, 2, 4, 10, 19, 33, 43, 47, 49, 50.

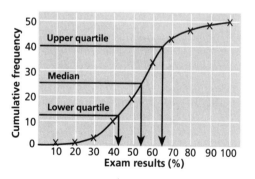

These data are then used to draw a **cumulative frequency graph**. The cumulative frequency is always put on the vertical scale, and the *top* value for that group on the horizontal scale. The graph usually forms a characteristic 'S' shape as shown here.

From this, useful statistics can be found. Reading across from the point halfway up the vertical scale gives the **median** on the horizontal scale, while reading across from the points one-quarter and three-quarters of the way up the scale gives the **lower quartile (LQ)** and **upper quartile (UQ)** respectively. The **interquartile range** is the difference between the upper quartile and the lower quartile. The cumulative frequency graph for the science examination example is shown here.

The **modal class** is the same sort of thing as the mode – it is the class with the most members in a grouped frequency table. The modal class is shown as the highest bar on a frequency diagram – don't forget that it covers a range of values, *not* a single value, and it may not even contain the actual modal value. For our example the modal class is 50–59.

4 A **pie chart** gives an alternative way of displaying information. A pie chart is a circle divided up into segments, each segment representing a value (or group of values) and the angle of the segment being the frequency. Remember there are 360° in the circle and so the angle for each segment is

$$\text{Angle of segment} = \frac{\text{number in group}}{\text{total number}} \times 360°$$

Again, don't forget to put a title and also label the segments.

The pie chart shown here gives the results of a survey of favourite colours, in which these six colours were all equally popular.

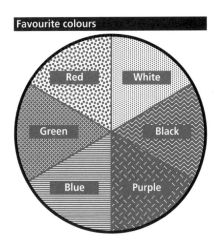

Favourite colours

Red White Green Black Blue Purple

5 **Scatter diagrams** are used to see if there is a connection between two sets of values, such as height and weight, as shown below.

Height (cm) and weight (kg) of 10 men

Height (cm)	165	168	170	170	173	180	183	185	188	190
Weight (kg)	65.8	63.6	76.2	73.4	68.1	77.0	65.6	69.6	78.5	81.7

As the low values of height seem generally to have a low weight and the high values of height seem generally to have a high weight, there does appear to be a connection between height and weight in the diagram.

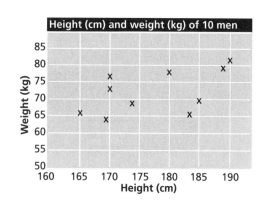

6 **Probability** is simply 'how likely something is to happen'. A scale from 0 to 1 is used for it:

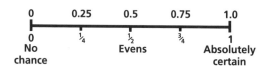

In other words,

If an event is bound to happen the probability is 1
If an event will never happen the probability is 0

One way of finding the probability is

$$\text{Probability of event happening} = \frac{\text{number of ways the event can happen}}{\text{number of possible outcomes}}$$

We can also use probability to predict how many times something is likely to happen.

7 When we have two events (say, A and B) which are independent we can calculate the probabilities using the following connection. If Pr(A) represents the probability of event A happening and Pr(B) represents the probability of event B happening, then

$$Pr(A \text{ or } B) = Pr(A) + Pr(B)$$
$$Pr(A \text{ and } B) = Pr(A) \times Pr(B)$$

3 Sometimes it is helpful to draw a diagram showing all possible outcomes. The best type of diagram is a **tree diagram**. Here is a tree diagram representing the spinning of a three-sided spinner, which has different-coloured sides, red (R), green (G) and blue (B). It is spun three times:

This shows that there are 27 possible outcomes, all of which are equally likely to occur. What is the probability of getting each colour once? From the asterisks, the probability is

$$\frac{6}{27} = \frac{2}{9}$$

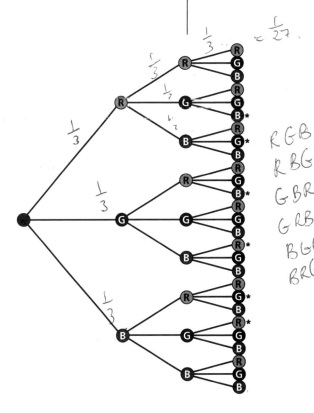

RGB
RBG
GBR
GRB
BGR
BRG

How to Do It

1 a The school hockey team scored the following number of goals in 10 matches:

    2 3 1 0 3 1 5 2 0 1

Find: (i) the mean number of goals scored per match;
(ii) the median number of goals scored;
(iii) the modal number of goals scored.

Solution

(i) Mean $= (2+3+1+0+3+1+5+2+0+1) \div 10 = 1.8$ goals per match

*'Here there
were as many
occasions
where the
score was
more than 1.5
goals per
match as when
there were
less. This is
always a
feature of the
median, as it is
a 'middle
value'*

(ii) For the median, arrange the values in order:

$$0 \quad 0 \quad 1 \quad 1 \quad 1 \quad 2 \quad 2 \quad 3 \quad 3 \quad 5$$

The median score is between 1 and 2, so the median is

$$(1+2) \div 2 = 1.5 \text{ goals per match}$$

(iii) The mode, the most common or popular score, is 1 goal per match.

b Two tests were given to a group of 10 students and the results were:

Test A   mean 8.2   standard deviation 1.9

Test B   mean 7.5

marks: 6 7 9 8 7 8 9 6 8 7

(i) Find the standard deviation for test B.

(ii) What do you deduce about the two tests from these results?

Solution

(i)

x	6	7	9	8	7	8	9	6	8	7
$d = 7.5 - x$	1.5	0.5	−1.5	−0.5	0.5	−0.5	−1.5	1.5	−0.5	0.5
d^2	2.25	0.25	2.25	0.25	0.25	0.25	2.25	2.25	0.25	0.25

$$\text{Standard deviation} = \sqrt{\frac{10.5}{10}} = \sqrt{1.05} = 1.02$$

(ii) The results suggest that the average student did better on test A than on test B. However, the marks for test A are more widespread than for test B, which suggests that test A may be a better test to use to distinguish between students.

2a The shoe sizes of 32 members of a club are

8 10 6 7 7 8 9 8

7   7 6 7 5 8 7 7

6   9 7 8 6 7 8 5

7   8 7 5 8 6 7 9

Produce a frequency table and find the mode.

Solution

Size	5	6	7	8	9	10
Frequency	3	5	12	8	3	1

The mode = size 7.

b The weights of 50 men, correct to the nearest kilogram, are shown here:

```
67  57  59  72  79  64  70  74  77  79
65  68  76  83  61  63  57  71  75  64
68  73  81  86  76  71  68  67  52  74
70  66  55  66  88  65  63  69  74  66
61  62  71  64  71  67  84  54  68  63
```

Draw a tally chart and grouped frequency table for groups 50–54, 55–59, etc. State the modal class.

Solution

Weight group	Tally	Frequency
50–54	II	2
55–59	IIII	4
60–64	JHT IIII	9
65–69	JHT JHT III	13
70–74	JHT JHT I	11
75–79	JHT I	6
80–84	III	3
85–89	II	2
	Total	50

The modal class is the class 65–69 kg.

'Note how the modal value is the highest bar'

3a

Draw a frequency diagram for the information in question 2a on pages 52–53.

Solution

The highest frequency is 12 so we need to choose a vertical scale to cope with this:

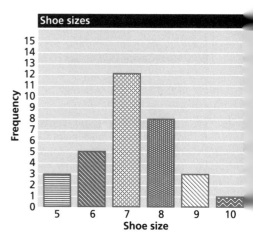

b Draw a frequency diagram for the grouped classes in question 2b on page 53, and estimate the mean weight of the men.

Solution

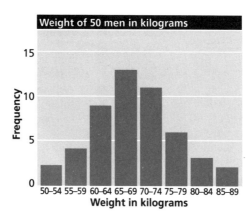

To estimate the mean, we need the mid-values of each of the classes with the frequency, as shown in the table at the top of the page opposite.

Class	Mid-value	Frequency	Freq. × mid-value
50–54	52	2	104
55–59	57	4	228
60–64	62	9	558
65–69	67	13	871
70–74	72	11	792
75–79	77	6	462
80–84	82	3	246
85–89	87	2	174
	Totals	50	3435

The estimate of the mean $= 3435 \div 50 = 68.7 \, \text{kg}$

4 a The pie chart shows how 160 men travel from home to the factory where they work. How many men travel by train?

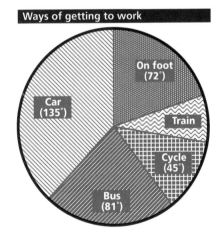

Ways of getting to work

On foot (72°)

Car (135°)

Train

Cycle (45°)

Bus (81°)

Solution
Since all the angles should total 360°, the angle for the train is

$$360° - (72° + 135° + 81° + 45°) = 27°$$

360° represents 160 people, so 27° represents

$$\frac{160}{360} \times 27 = 12 \text{ people}$$

b The sales in a baker's shop for one week were White bread £160, wholemeal bread £140, cakes £100, flour £52, biscuits £28. Draw a pie chart to represent this information.

Solution

Total sales = £480 so the angle for 'White bread' is

$$\frac{160}{480} \times 360 = 120°$$

Similar calculations for the others give:

Wholemeal 105°   Cakes 75°   Flour 39°   Biscuits 21°

Here is the pie chart:

A baker's shop sales

'Check that the angles add up to 360°'

5 Twelve pupils were to take two mathematics test papers. Unfortunately one was absent for the first paper and another was absent for the second. Here are the marks for the pupils:

Pupil	A	B	C	D	E	F	G	H	J	K	L	M
Paper 1	77	52	62	44	50	53	abs	68	71	60	38	59
Paper 2	76	49	abs	34	39	44	36	66	68	60	34	50

Plot a scatter diagram for the results where both marks are known and by drawing a line that 'fits' the points give estimates of the likely marks for the two absent pupils.

Solution

Pupil A is entered on the graph at a point whose co-ordinates represent 77 on Paper 1 and 76 on Paper 2. We can do the same for all others except C and G. When the ten points are plotted, we see that there is a distinct tendency for high marks in one test to be associated with high marks in the other test – indeed, the points could be regarded as being scattered around a '**line of best fit**', so we do our best to draw in that line. Having done so, that line can be regarded as a sort of predictor line. In other words, if we have results of only one test, the line gives us a reasonable way of estimating what the other result might be. We cannot be certain, of course, but it is the best prediction that we can make. Using this technique, we see that candidate C got 62 on Paper 1 and an estimated 55 on Paper 2, and candidate G got 36 on Paper 2 and an estimated 42 on paper 1.

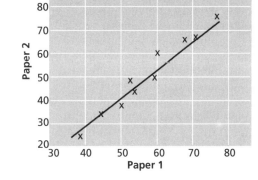

'To get a line of best fit, draw it so that about half the crosses are above the line and half below'

6 Ten counters have the numbers 1 to 10 printed on them. They are placed in a bag and one is picked out at random. What is the probability that the number on it is:

    (i) odd   (ii) a multiple of 3   (iii) a prime number

Solution

(i) The odd numbers from 1 to 10 are

    1 3 5 7 9 (5 of them)

so $\Pr(\text{odd}) = \dfrac{5}{10}$

The probability of its being odd $= \frac{1}{2}$ or 0.5   (some would write 50%).

(ii) The multiples of 3 are

    3 6 9 (3 of them)

The probability of a multiple of 3 is $\frac{3}{10}$ or 0.3.

(iii) The prime numbers are

    2 3 5 7 (4 of them)

The probability of a prime number is $\frac{4}{10}$ or 0.4.

7 A box contains 7 red and 12 yellow counters. Two are selected. What is the probability that they are both yellow?

'What you must be sure of when you do calculations like this is whether you add these probabilities or multiply them'

Solution

$$\Pr(\text{Yellow}_1) = \frac{12}{19} \qquad \Pr(\text{Yellow}_2) = \frac{11}{18} \quad \text{(assume first was yellow)}$$

The probability of both being yellow is

$$\frac{12}{19} \times \frac{11}{18} = \frac{22}{57}$$

8 A bag contains three red and two green fruit-drops. Draw a tree diagram to show the result of taking one sweet and then a second, without replacing the first sweet. What is the probability of:

    (i) two red   (ii) two green   (iii) one of each

Solution

Method 1
(For the first selection of sweet we could have chosen any of the five sweets – three red and two green. However, as a result of having taken a sweet, and not replacing it, we have only four sweets to select from: how many red and how many green depends upon what was taken the first time. If the first was a red then there is a choice only from two red and two green, whereas if the first had been a green there would be a choice from three red and one green.)

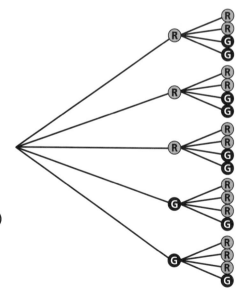

    (i) Of the 20 outcomes 6 have
        2 reds so probability
        of 2 reds is 0.3.
    (ii) Of the 20 outcomes 2 have
        2 greens so probability
        of 2 greens is 0.1.
    (iii) Of the 20 outcomes 12 are
        one of each so probability
        of one of each is 0.6.

Method 2

An alternative tree which is simpler to draw is one that shows the probabilities:

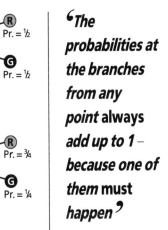

The probabilities that are shown are always the probabilities for the event happening assuming that the previous part has happened.

So we have:

(i) Probability of 2 reds $= \text{Pr}(R_1 \text{ \& } R_2)$

$$= \text{Pr}(R_1) \times \text{Pr}(R_2)$$
$$= \tfrac{3}{5} \times \tfrac{1}{2}$$
$$= \tfrac{3}{10} \text{ or } 0.3$$

(ii) Probability of 2 greens $= \text{Pr}(G_1 \text{ \& } G_2)$

$$= \text{Pr}(G_1) \times \text{Pr}(G_2)$$
$$= \tfrac{2}{5} \times \tfrac{1}{4}$$
$$= \tfrac{1}{10} \text{ or } 0.1$$

(iii) Probability of a red and a green or a green and a red

$$= \text{Pr}((R_1 \text{ \& } G_2) \text{ or } (G_1 \text{ \& } R_2))$$
$$= \text{Pr}(R_1) \times \text{Pr}(G_2) + \text{Pr}(G_1) \times \text{Pr}(R_2)$$
$$= \tfrac{3}{5} \times \tfrac{1}{2} + \tfrac{2}{5} \times \tfrac{3}{4}$$
$$= \tfrac{3}{10} + \tfrac{3}{10} = \tfrac{6}{10} \text{ or } 0.6$$

'The probabilities at the branches from any point always add up to 1 – because one of them must happen'

Do It Yourself

1 a The heights of nine girls (in centimetres) are

169   162   171   166   162   178   179   169   162

Find   (i)   the mean height;
        (ii)   the median height;
        (iii) the modal height.

b The number of goals scored by a football team in 12 consecutive matches were

1   1   4   0   0   2   5   3   0   2   6   0

Find: (i)   the mean number of goals;
         (ii)   the median number of goals;
         (iii) the modal number of goals.

c The heights, in metres, of members of the Rovers football team are:

1.80   1.73   1.58   1.64   1.72   1.76   1.84   1.65   1.73   1.76   1.60

(i) Find the mean and standard deviation of these heights.
(ii) The results for the United football team are:

mean 1.73 metres   standard deviation 0.025 metres

Which of the teams probably has the tallest player?

2 The frequency table below shows the number of pints of milk delivered on one day to the houses in Lime Avenue:

Number of pints delivered	0	1	2	3	4	5
Frequency	15	32	13	10	2	1

(i) Draw a bar chart to illustrate these data.
(ii) How many houses are there in Lime Avenue?
(iii) How many houses received some milk on the day in question?
(iv) How many pints of milk were delivered to Lime Avenue?

3 The number of words in each line of a page of the book *Journey to the Centre of the Earth* by Jules Verne are shown below. Form a frequency table and draw a bar chart of the results.

```
 9  8  6   8  5  9   1  10   9  10
10  8  1   1  3  6   6  10  12   3
 8  3  9  12  2  8  11  10   9  11
```

4 a A survey was done on 360 people to find out what they used to heat their houses. The results are shown on the right. Draw a pie chart to illustrate these data.

Fuel	Number of houses
Coal	40
Electricity	80
Gas	145
Oil	95

b This pie chart shows the sales figures of a company in various countries. If the sales in the UK amounted to £2 700 000 find the total sales figures for each of the other countries.

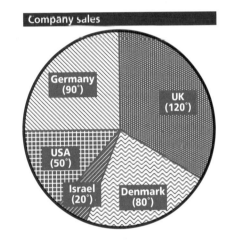

Company sales

c In 1992, 35% of the assets of a company were in Switzerland, 30% in the UK, 20% in North America and the rest were elsewhere. Draw a pie chart to illustrate these data.

5 A group of eight language students were given tests in French and German:

Pupil	1	2	3	4	5	6	7	8
French	10	31	37	11	26	18	15	22
German	9	34	35	15	26	20	14	21

Draw a scatter diagram and on it draw the line of 'best fit'.
If another pupil only did the French test and scored 17, what mark would you estimate if he had done the German?

6 Two unbiased dice, one red and the other blue, are used in a game. The red dice is marked 1 1 1 2 2 3 and the blue dice is marked 1 2 3 3 5 5. Complete the table on the right showing the possible sums of the two dice:

Blue \ Red	1	1	1	2	2	3
1	2	2	2	3	3	4
2	3	3	3	4	4	5
3	4	4	4	5	5	6
3	4	4	4	5	5	6
5	6	6	6	7	7	8
5	6	6	6	7	7	8

(i) What is the probability of getting a score of 6?

(ii) What is the probability of the two dice showing the same result?

(iii) At the end of the game Trish needs 4 and Neeva needs 5. Who is more likely to win and why?

7 In a vehicle park there are 100 vehicles – 85 are cars, 10 are lorries and 5 are buses. If they are all equally likely to leave, what is the probability that:

(i) A bus leaves first.

(ii) A car leaves after a bus has left first.

8 a A bag contains six 20p coins and three 50p coins. Two coins are selected at random. Draw a tree to illustrate this and use it to find the probability that:

(i) both coins are 20p coins.

(ii) both coins are 50p coins.

(iii) the first is a 20p coin and the second is a 50p coin.

(iv) there is exactly one 20p coin.

b A coin is spun three times. Draw a tree to illustrate all the possible results. Find the probability of getting:

(i) 3 heads;

(ii) 2 heads and a tail in any order.

Graphs

Things You Need to Know

1 The equation of a **straight line graph** can always be written in the form

$$y = mx + c$$

where m is the gradient and c is the point it crosses the y-axis (the y-axis intercept). If the gradient is *positive*, the line slopes *upwards* when going left to right, if the gradient is *negative*, it slopes *downwards* when going left to right, and if the gradient is 0 the line is horizontal.

2 The **gradient** is found by drawing a right-angled triangle using the straight line as the hypotenuse and lines parallel to the x- and y-axes to form the right angle:

$$\text{Gradient} = \frac{\text{change in } y \text{ values}}{\text{change in } x \text{ values}}$$

$$= \frac{9}{3}$$

$$= 3$$

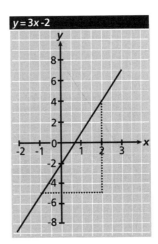

$y = 3x - 2$

63

When two lines are perpendicular, their gradients multiply to always give the value -1. So, if m_1 is the gradient of one line and m_2 is the gradient of the other line, they are perpendicular if

$$m_1 \times m_2 = -1$$

(This fact can be used to find the gradient of a line perpendicular to a given line.)

The gradient of a distance–time graph (see page 67) gives the velocity at that moment.

The gradient for a velocity–time graph (see page 67) gives the acceleration; if it is negative then the object is slowing down.

3 When drawing a graph always draw a **table of values** to produce the y-value from the x-value. For the graph $y = 3x - 2$ the table is as follows:

x	-2	-1	0	1	2	3
$3x$	-6	-3	0	3	6	9
-2	-2	-2	-2	-2	-2	-2
$y = 3x - 2$	-8	-5	-2	1	4	7

If we knew that it was a straight line, then we wouldn't need to calculate all of these values; we would only need three (the third is to check on the other two).

The graph of $y = x^2 + 3x - 2$ is not a straight line, so we would have to calculate several values, as shown at the top of the opposite page. (To draw this graph, you would calculate some further values for $x = -2.5$, $x = -1.5$, $x = 0.5$ in order to get as smooth a graph as possible.)

'Don't forget to label the axes of any graph and put a title'

x		−3	−2	−1	0	1	2	3
x^2		9	4	1	0	1	4	9
$3x$		−9	−6	−3	0	3	6	9
−2		−2	−2	−2	−2	−2	−2	−2
$y = x^2 + 3x - 2$		−2	−4	−4	−2	2	8	16

Equations like

$$y = x^2 + 1$$

produce curved graphs, as shown on the right. Below is a table of values for it.

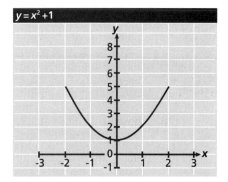

$y = x^2 + 1$

x	−2	−1	0	1	2
x^2	4	1	0	1	4
+1	+1	+1	+1	+1	+1
$y = x^2 + 1$	5	2	1	2	5

All graphs with the highest power of x being 2 will have a shape like the one above – it is called a **parabola**.

We can also get curves for equations known as **reciprocal equations,** like

$$y = \frac{24}{x}$$

Here is a table of values for it; the graph is known as a **hyperbola**.

x	−12	−8	−6	−4	−3	−2	−1	1	2	3	4	6	8	12
y	−2	−3	−4	−6	−8	−12	−24	24	12	8	6	4	3	2

'No value is given for x = 0, the reason being that there isn't one! Dividing by 0 is not allowed'

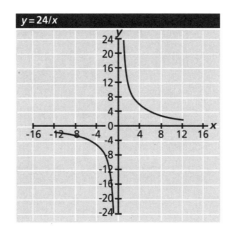

5   Gradients also apply to curves, but of course the gradient changes depending upon where on the curve we are. To find the gradient at a particular point on a curve we draw a tangent to the curve at that point and then find the gradient of the tangent line in the usual way. The diagram below shows the gradient being found at the point on the curve where $x = 1$.

The gradient at $x = 1$ is

$$\frac{4}{2} = 2$$

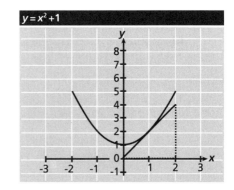

5 Graphs can be used to solve equations. The simplest form of equation might be one like

$$x^2 + 5x - 6 = 0$$

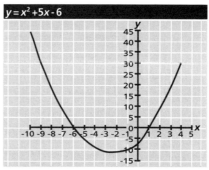

For this draw the graph of $y = x^2 + 5x - 6$. Draw the graph and find where it crosses the x-axis (i.e. where $y = 0$):

From the graph $x = -6$ or 1.

We can also use graphs to solve **simultaneous equations** (see page 145). Shown below are the graphs of two lines.

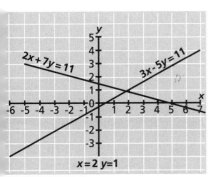

The line

$$3x - 5y = 1$$

is all the points that satisfy this equation. Similarly, the line

$$2x + 7y = 11$$

is all the points that satisfy this equation. So where the two lines intersect gives a point that satisfies *both* equations – hence the values of x and y solve both equations at the same time (or *simultaneously*).

7 Graphs can be used to help solve problems involving travel. Two types of graph are used. One shows the connection between the distance from some fixed point and the time taken (called a **distance–time graph**) and the other shows the connection between the velocity and time (called a **velocity–time graph**). Two words that you should know the meaning of are 'velocity' and 'acceleration'.

Velocity – Basically this is speed, but with the direction of the movement taken into account, measured in metres per second (m/s). A ship steaming north and another ship steaming east at 30 knots both have the same speed but as they have different directions of travel, their velocities are not the same.

Acceleration – This is how quickly the velocity is changing, measured in metres per second per second (m/s²).

Here is a distance–time graph showing Jim taking his dog for a walk. From this you can see that they took $10\frac{1}{2}$ minutes (630 seconds) and stopped four times, walked to a furthest point of 400 m and arrived back home at the end (because, after 630 seconds, distance from home is zero).

The gradient of the graph at any point will give the velocity at that moment (in this case the velocity will be in metres per second). If its value is negative then this means they are coming back to the starting point. If gradient = 0 then they have stopped.

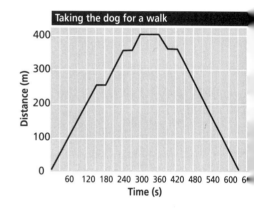

Here is a velocity–time graph of Bill taking a journey up the motorway for the first 10 minutes of the journey. This graph tells a story of speeding up, slowing down and travelling at the same speed. In the first 60 seconds the speed increases from 0 to 20 m/s, then stays at 20 m/s for $1\frac{1}{2}$ minutes. The speed then increases from 20 m/s to 30 m/s taking 60 seconds. This speed is maintained for a minute, after which the speed decreases to 25 m/s – and so on.

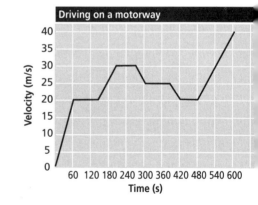

The gradient of the graph at any point will give the acceleration of the vehicle at that moment (in this case the units are m/s²) – don't forget to use the units on the axes. A positive acceleration means the velocity is increasing, a negative value means the velocity is decreasing and if it is 0 then he is travelling at a constant speed.

With a velocity–time graph, the area of a shape is a combination of the units of time and velocity formed by multiplying them; if time and velocity are multiplied, this gives the distance travelled. Hence, if we need to find the distance travelled for a particular velocity–time graph, we work out the area under the curve. In the example, the distance travelled in the 10 minutes on the motorway is given by adding up the areas marked A, B, C, D, E, F, G, H and J marked in the diagram; these shapes are trapezia and quadrilaterals with a triangle.

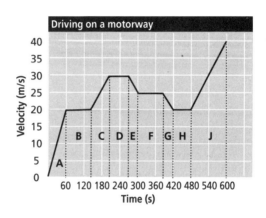

'We read m/s² as 'metres per second squared' or 'metres per second per second'

Area A $= 0.5 \times 60 \times 20$ $= 600$
Area B $= 20 \times 90$ $= 1800$
Area C $= 0.5 \times (20 + 30) \times 60$ $= 1500$
Area D $= 30 \times 60$ $= 1800$
Area E $= 0.5 \times (30 + 25) \times 30$ $= 825$
Area F $= 25 \times 90$ $= 2250$
Area G $= 0.5 \times (25 + 20) \times 30$ $= 675$
Area H $= 20 \times 60$ $= 1200$
Area J $= 0.5 \times (20 + 40) \times 120 = 3600$

This gives a total distance of 14 250 m $= 14.25$ km

(**Note:** seconds were used for the time because the speed was given as metres per second. This will also mean that the distance calculated will be in metres.)

Bill's average speed over this time is

$$\frac{14\,250}{600}\,\text{m/s} = 23.75\,\text{m/s} \quad \text{(or 85.5 km/h)}$$

How to Do It

1 **a** The following equations represent straight line graphs. In each case find the gradient and the y-axis intercept without drawing the graph.

> (i) $y = 3x - 5$ (ii) $3y = 6x - 2$
> (iii) $5y = 2x + 10$ (iv) $2x + 3y = 5$

Solution

(i) For $y = 3x - 5$, the gradient $= 3$ and the y-axis intercept $= -5$.
(ii) For $3y = 6x - 2$, this becomes

$$y = 2x - \frac{2}{3}$$

so the gradient $= 2$ and the y-axis intercept $= \frac{2}{3}$.
(iii) For $5y = 2x + 10$, the gradient $= \frac{2}{5}$ and the y-axis intercept $= 2$.
(iv) For $2x + 3y = 5$, this becomes

$$y = -\frac{2}{3}x + \frac{5}{3}$$

so the gradient $= -\frac{2}{3}$ and the y-axis intercept $= \frac{5}{3}$.

b What is the equation of the following straight line graphs (draw a sketch):

> (i) gradient $= 2$ y-axis intercept $= -1$
>
> (ii) gradient $= \frac{3}{5}$ y-axis intercept $= 1$
>
> (iii) gradient $= \frac{4}{3}$ y-axis intercept $= \frac{1}{3}$

Solution

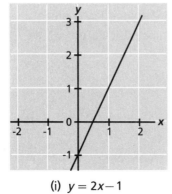

(i) $y = 2x - 1$

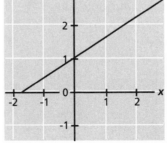

(ii) $5y = 3x + 5$

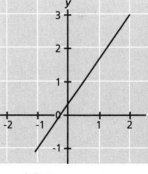

(iii) $3y = 4x + 1$

2a Here are some points that are on a straight line graph. Plot the points and draw the straight line to find the equation of the line.

x	2	4	6	8	10	12
y	10	16	22	28	34	40

'When we know we are dealing with a straight line graph, then we actually need plot only two points. In practice, we always plot three so we have a check'

Solution

The y-axis intercept is 4 and the gradient = 3 so

$$y = 3x + 4$$

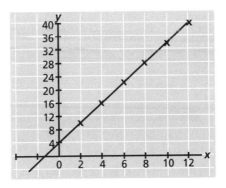

b During an experiment to verify Ohm's law the following results were obtained:

E (volts)	0	1.0	2.0	2.5	3.7	4.1	5.9	6.8	8.0
I (amps)	0	0.24	0.5	0.63	0.92	1.05	1.48	1.70	2.05

Draw the best straight line through the points and find its equation.

Solution

The y-axis intercept is 0 and the gradient is $\frac{1}{4}$, so

$$I = \tfrac{1}{4}E$$

As the best straight line is drawn in by eye, it is possible that you will get a slightly different answer. This came out as a nice fraction, but it could have been a decimal value – you might get a gradient of 0.26, giving $I = 0.26E$.

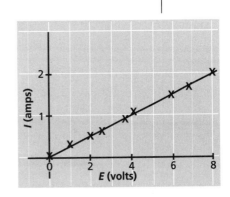

71

3 Produce a table of values for the equation $y = 2x^2 - x - 2$, with x going from -3 to 3 in steps of 1. Using the table, between what two pairs of values of x does $y = 0$?

Solution

x	-3	-2	-1	0	1	2	3
$2x^2$	18	8	2	0	2	8	18
$-x$	3	2	1	0	-1	-2	-3
-2	-2	-2	-2	-2	-2	-2	-2
$y = 2x^2 - x - 2$	19	8	1	-2	-1	4	13

The value of y changes from 1 to -2 for $x = -1$ to $x = 0$ and it changes from -1 to 4 for $x = 1$ to $x = 2$, so the two pairs of values of x are:

$x = -1, x = 0$
$x = 1, x = 2$

4 Draw the graph of $y = 1 - 2x - x^2$, between $x = -4$ and $x = 4$. Hence solve the equations:

    (i) $1 - 2x - x^2 = 0$ (ii) $4 - 2x - x^2 = 0$ (iii) $4x^2 + 8x = 12$

Solution

x	-4	-3	-2	-1	0	1	2	3
1	1	1	1	1	1	1	1	1
$-2x$	8	6	4	2	0	-2	-4	-6
$-x^2$	-16	-9	-4	-1	0	-1	-4	-9
$y = 1 - 2x - x^2$	-7	-2	1	2	1	-2	-7	-14

The graph is shown here.

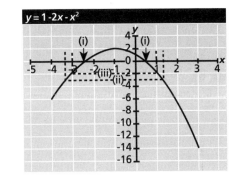

(i) $1-2x-x^2 = 0$

    Comparing this to the original

      $y = 1-2x-x^2$

$y = 0$

so looking at the graph line and finding where $y = 0$ gives

    $x = 0.4$ and $x = -2.4$

marked with (i) on the graph

(ii) $4-2x-x^2 = 0$

    This needs a little rearranging to make it like the original:

      $1-2x-x^2 = -3$

Comparing to the original equation, $y = -3$

so looking at the graph line and finding where $y = -3$ gives

    $x = 1.2$ and $x = -3.2$

marked with (ii) on the graph

(iii) $4x^2 + 8x = 12$

    This needs more than a little rearranging. First divide by 4:

      $x^2 + 2x = 3$

Rearranged, this is:

    $-3 = -2x-x^2$

Adding 1 to both sides:

    $-2 = 1-2x-x^2$

so $y = -2$ when this is compared to the original.
    Looking at the graph line where $y = -2$ gives:

    $x = 1$ or $x = -3$

marked with (iii) on the graph

5 Draw the graph of $y = x^2 - 3x + 7$ between $x = -4$ and $x = 4$. Find the gradient of the curve at the positions where $x = -3$ and $x = 2$.

Solution

x	-4	-3	-2	-1	0	1	2	3	4
x^2	16	9	4	1	0	1	4	9	16
$-3x$	12	9	6	3	0	-3	-6	-9	-12
7	7	7	7	7	7	7	7	7	7
$y = x^2 - 3x + 7$	35	25	17	11	7	5	5	7	11

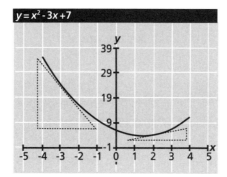

At $x = -3$ the gradient is -9
At $x = 2$ the gradient is 1

6a By drawing a suitable graph solve the equation $6x^2 - 7x - 5 = 0$.

Solution

The graph to plot is

$y = 6x^2 - 7x - 5$ and find where $y = 0$.

The solution to the equation is

$x = -0.5$ or 1.7

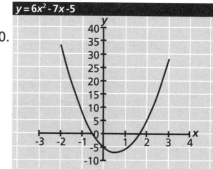

b Solve the following pair of simultaneous equations by drawing their graphs:

$$y = 9 + 3x - 2x^2$$
$$3y = 2x + 14$$

Solution

The graphs are drawn in the usual manner. Where the graphs intersect is a point or points that satisfy both equations at the same time. The two points are:

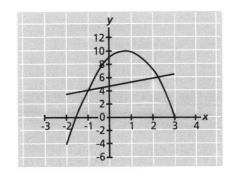

$x = 2.2, y = 6$ and $x = -1, y = 4$

If you substitute these values into the equations, you will find that, although $(-1, 4)$ is an exact solution, $(2.2, 6)$ is approximate. Solutions found using graphs are not as accurate as algebraic solutions.

'Only use graphs to solve simultaneous equations if you are told to in the question'

7a A cyclist starts from Hometown at 9.00 a.m. and cycles towards Worksville at a speed of 15 km/h. At 10.00 a.m. a motorist leaves Hometown to make the same journey, but he travels at 60 km/h. At what time does the motorist overtake the cyclist and how far from Hometown are they?

Solution

The motorist passes the cyclist at 10.20 a.m. at a distance of 20 km from Hometown.

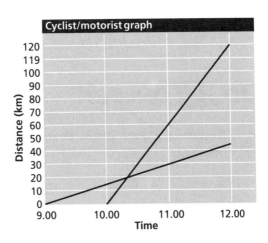

b The diagram shows a velocity–time graph. Find:

    (i) the acceleration after 5 seconds;

    (ii) the acceleration after 18 seconds;

    (iii) The maximum speed reached;

    (iv) total distance travelled in 50 seconds.

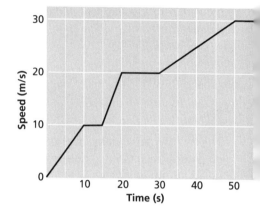

Solution

(i) Acceleration after 5 seconds is given by the gradient at 5 seconds and is

      $1 \, \text{m/s}^2$

(ii) Acceleration after 18 seconds (i.e. gradient at time 18 seconds) is

      $2 \, \text{m/s}^2$

(iii) Maximum speed $= 30 \, \text{m/s}$

(iv) Find area for each part and sum:

0 to 10 distance:	$0.5 \times 10 \times 10 = 50$
10 to 15 distance:	$10 \times 5 = 50$
15 to 20 distance:	$0.5 \times (10 + 20) \times 5 = 75$
20 to 30 distance:	$10 \times 20 = 200$
30 to 50 distance:	$0.5 \times (20 + 30) \times 20 = 500$

Total distance $= 875 \, \text{m}$.

Do It Yourself

1 Find the equation of the straight line given the gradient and y-axis intercept:

	Gradient	y-axis intercept
(i)	3	4
(ii)	-2	-2
(iii)	$-\frac{1}{2}$	3
(iv)	4	-6
(v)	-1	$-\frac{1}{4}$

2a For each of the graphs below find:
the gradient of the line;
the y-axis intercept.

(i) $y = 4x - 7$ (ii) $y = 2x + 9$ (iii) $y = 6x + 3$
(iv) $y = 5x - \frac{1}{2}$ (v) $y = \frac{1}{4}x - 2$ (vi) $y = 8 - x$

b The points A and B have coordinates $(-1, -4)$ and $(4, 1)$ respectively.

(i) Find the gradient of AB.
(ii) Using Pythagoras' theorem, calculate the length of AB.
(iii) Find the equation of the line AB.

3 (i) Copy and complete the following table for values of x^2 between -4 and 4:

x	-4	-3	-2	-1	0	1	2	3	4
x^2	16				0	1			

(ii) Draw the graph of $y = x^2$, for x-values between -4 and 4. Use your graph to find the square of 1.8 and the square root of 13.

4 Sketch the graph of $y = x^2 - 4x - 5$ for $-2 \leqslant x \leqslant 4$, and show clearly its axis of symmetry (see page 119).

5 Draw the graph of $y = 2x^2 - 5$ for values of x between -2 and 3. Find the gradient of the curve at the points where $x = -1$ and $x = 2$.

6a Solve graphically the following pairs of simultaneous equations; use appropriate values of x and let 1 cm represent 1 unit on both axes.

(i) $y = x$ $2x + 3y = 5$
(ii) $x + y + 2 = 0$ $y = x - 3$
(iii) $3x + y + 5 = 0$ $2x - 4y + 8 = 0$

'When you draw a line graph that is not a straight line always twist the graph paper round so that your hand is inside the curve – it will help you get a smoother curve'

b Draw the graph of $y = x^2$ and $y = 2x+1$ for values of x from -1 to $+3$. From the graph read the solutions to the equation

$$x^2 - 2x - 1 = 0$$

c Using a scale of 8 cm for one unit along the x- and y-axes, draw the graph of

$$y = \frac{1}{x}$$

for $0.5 \leqslant x \leqslant 2$. Show that the equation

$$x^2 - x - 1 = 0$$

can be turned into

$$x - 1 = \frac{1}{x}$$

Superimpose a suitable straight line graph on that of $y = \frac{1}{x}$ and use it to find the positive root of $x - 1 = \frac{1}{x}$.

7a A coach leaves Bristol at 09.45 to travel to Aberdeen, 480 miles away. The journey takes 8 hours and 20 minutes. What time does the coach arrive in Aberdeen, and what was its average speed?

b Mark left home at 6.30 a.m. to travel to the airport 115 miles away. He travelled the first 15 miles at an average speed of 45 miles/hour and the rest at an average of 40 miles/hour.

(i) At what time did he arrive, assuming he did not stop on the way?
(ii) What was his average speed for the whole journey?

c The graph shows Philip's journey from home to school. He walked to the bus stop, waited and then caught the bus to school.

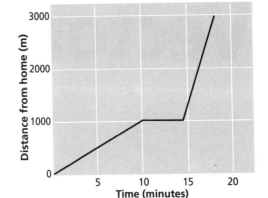

   (i) How long did it take him to walk to the bus stop?
   (ii) How long did he wait at the bus stop?
   (III) How far from home was he after 13 minutes?
   (iv) How far is it from the bus stop to school?

d A bee is flying with an initial velocity of 0.4 m/s. A gust of wind steadily increases the bee's velocity for 3 seconds until it is moving at 1 m/s. Its velocity then steadily decreases until it comes to a rest at the hive 5 seconds later.

   (i) Display this information on a velocity–time graph.
   (ii) Calculate the bee's acceleration between:
      (a) $t = 0$ seconds and $t = 3$ seconds;
      (b) $t = 3$ seconds and when it reaches the hive.

e Vicky runs for $1\frac{1}{2}$ hours at 12 km/h and then for 1 hour at 15 km/h and then finally for $\frac{1}{2}$ hour at 10 km/h.

   (i) How far does she run altogether?
   (ii) Draw a sketch graph to show her speed during her run.
   (iii) The next day she runs the same distance at a constant speed in the same time. What is this speed?

10 | **Vectors**

Things You Need to Know

1 A **vector** is a quantity that has two parts to it: magnitude (or size) and direction. Some examples are: a force (e.g. 2 newtons (N) upwards), or a velocity (e.g. 30 knots north-west).

We represent a vector by a line (whose length is proportional to the magnitude) drawn in the direction of the vector, as shown on the right.

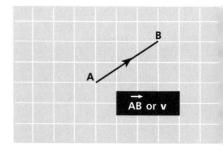

We write this as $\overrightarrow{AB}$ with the arrow above indicating the direction ('A towards B') or as a single lower-case letter, say **v**. When it is printed, the lower-case letter is shown in bold like this. When it is hand-written, it is underlined with a squiggly line.

2 The vector in the previous example could be described by the movement from A to B, i.e. 3 along and 2 up. This would be written as

$$\begin{pmatrix} 3 \\ 2 \end{pmatrix}$$

The top number always shows the horizontal movement and the bottom number the vertical movement. A positive number is to the right or upward, and a negative number is to the left or downward. This way of writing a vector is known as a **column vector**.

3 The **modulus** (an alternative name for the magnitude) of a vector can be calculated by using Pythagoras' theorem as follows:

$$\begin{pmatrix} 3 \\ 2 \end{pmatrix}$$

$$\begin{aligned} \text{Modulus} &= \sqrt{3^2 + 2^2} \\ &= \sqrt{13} \\ &= 3.61 \quad \text{(to 2 d.p.)} \end{aligned}$$

In order to indicate the modulus of a vector we use vertical lines around the vector – e.g. the modulus of the vector **t** would be $|t|$.

4 Generally the position of vectors is not important and two equal vectors just have to be equal in magnitude and direction. The vectors shown on the right are all equal.

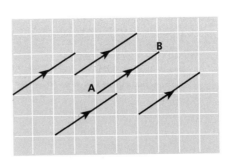

5 We can multiply a vector by a number, e.g. 2**u**. This is simply a vector with two times the magnitude of **u** and in the same direction.

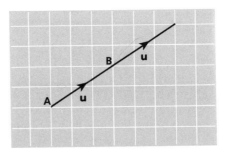

> '*The top number shows the horizontal movement and the bottom number the vertical movement*'

6 Vectors are added together in a special way by simply following the first vector with the second vector – the resultant being the single vector that goes from start to finish.

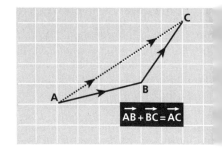

When written as numbers it looks like this:

$$\text{If} \qquad \overrightarrow{AB} = \begin{pmatrix} 4 \\ 1 \end{pmatrix}$$

$$\text{and} \qquad \overrightarrow{BC} = \begin{pmatrix} 2 \\ 3 \end{pmatrix}$$

$$\text{then} \quad \overrightarrow{AB} + \overrightarrow{BC} = \begin{pmatrix} 4 \\ 1 \end{pmatrix} + \begin{pmatrix} 2 \\ 3 \end{pmatrix}$$

$$= \begin{pmatrix} 4+2 \\ 1+3 \end{pmatrix}$$

$$= \begin{pmatrix} 6 \\ 4 \end{pmatrix}$$

7 Subtracting is much the same as adding, but the one being subtracted is drawn in the opposite direction to its normal direction (remember **a** − **b** is the same as **a** + −**b**):

$\overrightarrow{BC}$ is shown as $\overrightarrow{BX}$ where $\overrightarrow{BX}$ is the same size (or length) as $\overrightarrow{BC}$ but it is in the opposite direction.

$$\overrightarrow{AB} = \begin{pmatrix} 4 \\ 1 \end{pmatrix}$$

$$\overrightarrow{BC} = \begin{pmatrix} 2 \\ 3 \end{pmatrix}$$

$$\overrightarrow{AB} + \overrightarrow{BC} = \begin{pmatrix} 4 \\ 1 \end{pmatrix} - \begin{pmatrix} 2 \\ 3 \end{pmatrix}$$

$$= \begin{pmatrix} 4-2 \\ 1-3 \end{pmatrix}$$

$$= \begin{pmatrix} 2 \\ -2 \end{pmatrix}$$

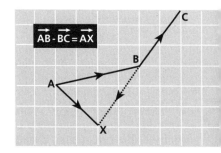

3 Some geometrical facts concerning vectors are:

(i) Two vectors are equal (in both magnitude and direction) if the two numbers (called the **components**) of each vector are the same, or if the lines representing the vectors are the same length and parallel.

(ii) Two vectors are parallel if the components are in the same proportion. For example:

$$\binom{5}{3} \text{ is parallel to } \binom{15}{9} \quad \binom{2\frac{1}{2}}{1\frac{1}{2}} \quad \binom{7\frac{1}{2}}{4\frac{1}{2}}$$

(iii) If a vector is a fraction of another vector then it is only the magnitude (or length of the line vector) that is affected; the direction remains the same. For example, find the mid-point of AB with A(2, 3) and B(8, 11):

$$\overrightarrow{AB} = \binom{6}{8} \quad \text{so} \quad \tfrac{1}{2}\overrightarrow{AB} = \binom{3}{4}$$

so the mid-point is $\binom{3}{4}$ from A, i.e. at (5, 7).

How to Do It

1 For each of the following vector quantities state its magnitude and direction:

(i) a journey of 3 miles on a bearing of 035°;

(ii) a force of 7 N applied at an angle of 75°;

(iii) a horizontal force of 12 N;

(iv) a displacement vertically of 10 units.

Solution

(i) Magnitude = 3 miles   Direction is 035°

(ii) Magnitude is 7 N   Direction is 70°

(iii) Magnitude is 12 N   Direction is horizontal

(iv) Magnitude of 10 units   Direction is vertical

2a On a grid draw and label each of the following vectors:

(i) $\overrightarrow{AB} = \binom{4}{3}$ (ii) $\mathbf{t} = \binom{5}{8}$ (iii) $\overrightarrow{LM} = \binom{-2}{-1}$ (iv) $\overrightarrow{XY} = \binom{3}{-4}$

Solution

b For each of the vectors illustrated in the diagram below write its label and as a column vector.

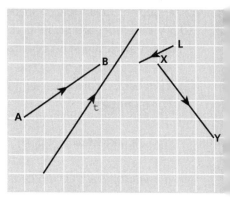

Solution

(i) $\overrightarrow{AB} = \begin{pmatrix} 4 \\ 2 \end{pmatrix}$

(ii) $\overrightarrow{DC} = \begin{pmatrix} -1 \\ 3 \end{pmatrix}$

(iii) $\overrightarrow{FE} = \begin{pmatrix} -3 \\ -3 \end{pmatrix}$

(iv) $\overrightarrow{GH} = \begin{pmatrix} -3 \\ 0 \end{pmatrix}$

(v) $\overrightarrow{KL} = \begin{pmatrix} 0 \\ -2 \end{pmatrix}$

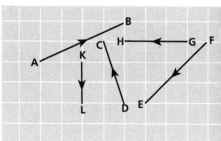

3 For each of the vectors in question 2(b) calculate the modulus.

Solution

(i) Modulus of $\overrightarrow{AB} = \begin{pmatrix} 4 \\ 2 \end{pmatrix} = \sqrt{4^2 + 2^2}$

$= \sqrt{20} = 4.47$

(ii) Modulus of $\overrightarrow{DC} = \begin{pmatrix} -1 \\ 3 \end{pmatrix} = \sqrt{(-1)^2 + 3^2}$

$= \sqrt{10} = 3.16$

(iii) Modulus of $\overrightarrow{FE} = \begin{pmatrix} -3 \\ -3 \end{pmatrix} = \sqrt{(-3)^2 + (-3)^2}$

$= \sqrt{18} = 4.24$

(iv) Modulus of $\overrightarrow{GH} = \begin{pmatrix} -3 \\ 0 \end{pmatrix} = \sqrt{(-3)^2 + 0^2}$

$= \sqrt{9} = 3$

(v) Modulus of $\overrightarrow{KL} = \begin{pmatrix} 0 \\ -2 \end{pmatrix} = \sqrt{0^2 + (-2)^2}$

$= \sqrt{4} = 2$

'Remember that when you square a negative number it becomes positive'

4 In the diagram find all the vectors

(i) equal to $\overrightarrow{AB}$;

(ii) equal to $\overrightarrow{CD}$.

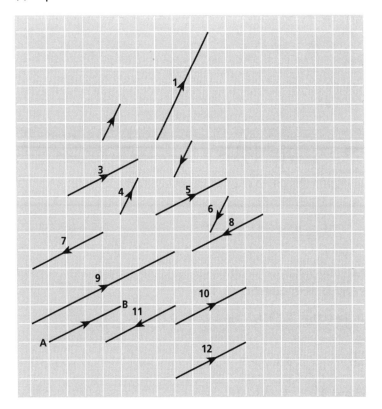

Solution

(i) Equal to $\overrightarrow{AB}$: the vectors are 3, 5, 10 and 12.

(ii) Equal to $\overrightarrow{CD}$: the vector is 4.

5 In the diagram for question 4 find a vector which is the same as

(i) equal to $2\overrightarrow{AB}$;

(ii) equal to $3\overrightarrow{CD}$.

Solution

(i) The vector is labelled 9.

(ii) The vector is labelled 1.

6 If $\mathbf{a} = \begin{pmatrix} 2 \\ -3 \end{pmatrix}$ and $\mathbf{b} = \begin{pmatrix} 5 \\ 7 \end{pmatrix}$, find by calculation:

    (i) $\mathbf{a} + \mathbf{b}$ (ii) $2\mathbf{a} + 5\mathbf{b}$

Solution

(i) $\mathbf{a} + \mathbf{b} = \begin{pmatrix} 2 \\ -3 \end{pmatrix} + \begin{pmatrix} 5 \\ 7 \end{pmatrix}$

$= \begin{pmatrix} 7 \\ 4 \end{pmatrix}$

(ii) $2\mathbf{a} + 5\mathbf{b} = 2\begin{pmatrix} 2 \\ -3 \end{pmatrix} + 5\begin{pmatrix} 5 \\ 7 \end{pmatrix}$

$= \begin{pmatrix} 4 \\ -6 \end{pmatrix} + \begin{pmatrix} 25 \\ 35 \end{pmatrix}$

$= \begin{pmatrix} 29 \\ 29 \end{pmatrix}$

7 Using $\mathbf{a}$ and $\mathbf{b}$ as in question 6, find:

    (i) $3\mathbf{a} - 3\mathbf{b}$ (ii) $\mathbf{b} - 2\mathbf{a}$

Solution

(i) $3\mathbf{a} - 3\mathbf{b} = 3\begin{pmatrix} 2 \\ -3 \end{pmatrix} - 3\begin{pmatrix} 5 \\ 7 \end{pmatrix}$

$= \begin{pmatrix} 6 \\ -9 \end{pmatrix} - \begin{pmatrix} 15 \\ 21 \end{pmatrix} = \begin{pmatrix} -9 \\ -30 \end{pmatrix}$

(ii) $\mathbf{b} - 2\mathbf{a} = \begin{pmatrix} 5 \\ 7 \end{pmatrix} - 2\begin{pmatrix} 2 \\ -3 \end{pmatrix}$

$= \begin{pmatrix} 5 \\ 7 \end{pmatrix} - \begin{pmatrix} 4 \\ -6 \end{pmatrix} = \begin{pmatrix} 1 \\ 13 \end{pmatrix}$

8 ABC is a triangle, with $\overrightarrow{AB} = \mathbf{b}$ and $\overrightarrow{AC} = \mathbf{c}$. The mid-points of AB and AC are X and Y respectively. Express in terms of $\mathbf{b}$ and $\mathbf{c}$:

    (i) $\overrightarrow{BC}$ (ii) $\overrightarrow{AX}$ (iii) $\overrightarrow{AY}$ (iv) $\overrightarrow{XY}$

Solution

(i) $\overrightarrow{BC} = \overrightarrow{BA} + \overrightarrow{AC} = -(\overrightarrow{AB}) + \overrightarrow{AC}$
$= -\mathbf{b} + \mathbf{c} = \mathbf{c} - \mathbf{b}$

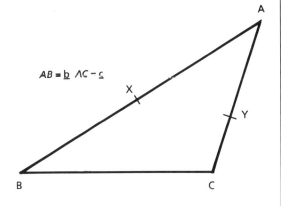

$AB = \underline{b} \ \ AC - \underline{c}$

(ii) $\overrightarrow{AX} = \tfrac{1}{2}\overrightarrow{AB} = \tfrac{1}{2}\mathbf{b}$

(iii) $\overrightarrow{AY} = \tfrac{1}{2}\overrightarrow{AC} = \tfrac{1}{2}\mathbf{c}$

(iv) $\overrightarrow{XY} = \overrightarrow{XA} + \overrightarrow{AY} = -(\overrightarrow{AX}) + \overrightarrow{AY}$
$= -(\tfrac{1}{2}\mathbf{b}) + (\tfrac{1}{2}\mathbf{c}) = -\tfrac{1}{2}\mathbf{b} + \tfrac{1}{2}\mathbf{c}$
$= \tfrac{1}{2}(-\mathbf{b} + \mathbf{c}) = \tfrac{1}{2}(\mathbf{c} - \mathbf{b})$

Since $\overrightarrow{BC} = \mathbf{c} - \mathbf{b}$ and $\overrightarrow{XY} = \tfrac{1}{2}(\mathbf{c} - \mathbf{b})$, this means that XY and BC are parallel and XY is half the length of BC.

Do It Yourself

1 For each of the following vector quantities, state its magnitude and direction:

    (i) A journey northeast of 5 miles

    (ii) A weight of 3 kilograms

    (iii) A straight path of length 50 metres going in a southwesterly direction, with a cyclist travelling along 80% of it

2 The four points in a plane are A(1, 3), B(3, 4), C(−1, −3) and D(5, 0). Write the vectors

    $\overrightarrow{AB}$ $\overrightarrow{AC}$ $\overrightarrow{CD}$ $\overrightarrow{BD}$ $\overrightarrow{DA}$

Which of the vectors are parallel to each other?

3 If A(3, 4), B(1, 6), C(5, 4) are the points of a triangle, find the vectors and the modulus:

    (i) $\overrightarrow{AB}$ (ii) $\overrightarrow{BC}$ (iii) $\overrightarrow{CA}$

4 The quadrilateral ABCD is defined by the points A(1, 2), B(4, 8), C(1, 1) and D(2, 3). Show that $\overrightarrow{AB}$ is parallel to $\overrightarrow{CD}$. What is the ratio of their lengths? Do the four points form a parallelogram?

5 If X is the point (3, 5), Y is point (7, −3) and O is the origin

    (i) Find the following vectors: $\mathbf{x} = \overrightarrow{OX}$, $\mathbf{y} = \overrightarrow{OY}$

    (ii) Find $2(\mathbf{x}+\mathbf{y})$ and $2\mathbf{x}+2\mathbf{y}$

    (iii) Find $\frac{1}{2}(\mathbf{x}+\mathbf{y})$. Is this the vector $\overrightarrow{OM}$, where M is the mid-point of the line XY?

6 a Two forces are given by

$$\mathbf{f} = \begin{pmatrix} 2 \\ 8 \end{pmatrix} \qquad \mathbf{g} = \begin{pmatrix} 3 \\ 4 \end{pmatrix}$$

Find the single force $\mathbf{h}$ equal to $\mathbf{f}+\mathbf{g}$. Find $|\mathbf{f}|$, $|\mathbf{g}|$ and $|\mathbf{h}|$.

b A river flows at 3 km/h and a man rows at 5 km/h. If he points directly across the river find his actual speed and direction. (Hint: The vector could be $\begin{pmatrix} 0 \\ 3 \end{pmatrix}$ for the river velocity and $\begin{pmatrix} 5 \\ 0 \end{pmatrix}$ for the rower. Assume 'up' is across the river and the river flows from left to right.)

7 If A is the point (2, 6), B the point (6, 8) and C the point (4, 12), and if $\mathbf{a}$ is the vector $\overrightarrow{OA}$, $\mathbf{b}$ the vector $\overrightarrow{OB}$ and $\mathbf{c}$ the vector $\overrightarrow{OC}$, where O is the origin, find:

    (i) $\mathbf{a}-2\mathbf{b}$

    (ii) $3\mathbf{a}-2\mathbf{b}-\mathbf{c}$

8 a If we have the points A(1, 1), B(2, 3) and C(1, 2), find the point D such that ABCD is a parallelogram. Are there any other possibilities for D?

b L(1, 2), M(5, 4), N(6, 2) and P(2, 0) are the four vertices of a quadrilateral. Show that they form a parallelogram. By considering the lengths of the diagonals, show that the parallelogram is in fact a rectangle.

Angles and Loci

Things You Need to Know

1 The following basic facts about angles:

   (i) The angles on a straight line total 180°.

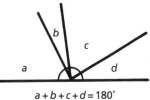

$$a + b + c + d = 180°$$

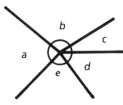

   (ii) The angles round a point total 360°. $a + b + c + d + e = 360°$

   (iii) The use of the names acute (less than 90°), right angle (equal to 90°), obtuse (greater than 90° and less than 180°) and reflex (greater than 180°).

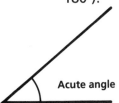

Acute angle

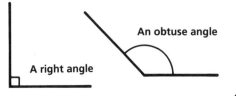

A right angle

An obtuse angle

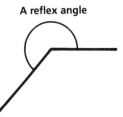

A reflex angle

(iv) When two lines cross, opposite angles are equal.

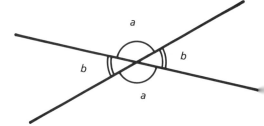

(v) Parallel lines are straight lines that never meet no matter how much they are extended – they are marked with arrows to indicate which lines are parallel.

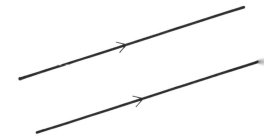

(vi) When a line crosses a pair of parallel lines there is a relationship between the angles formed – some are equal and others add up to 180°. In the diagram, $a + b = 180°$.

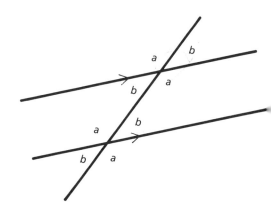

2 A **locus** is the path followed (or traced out) by a point as it moves according to some rule. Here are some examples:

(i) The locus of a point such that it is always the same distance from a line (don't forget that it could be either side of the line) gives a pair of lines parallel to the original line.

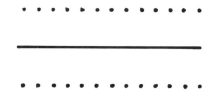

(ii) The locus of a point such that it is always the same distance from some fixed point gives a circle.

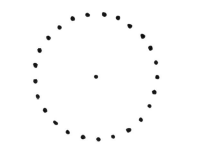

(iii) The locus of a point such that it is equidistant from a pair of lines gives the bisectors of the angles between the lines.

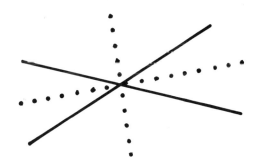

How to Do It

1 In each of the following diagrams find the unknown angle (or angles), and state whether it is an acute angle, an obtuse angle, a reflex angle or a right angle. (*Note*: None of the diagrams are accurate.)

(i)

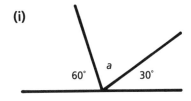

(ii)

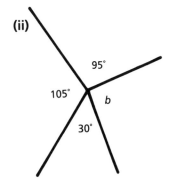

(iii)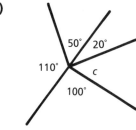

(iv)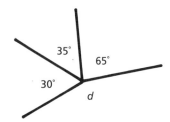

(v)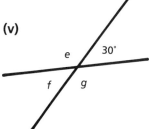

(vi)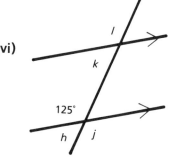

Solution

(i) The angles on a straight line
total 180°, so

$$60° + a + 30° = 180°$$
$$a = 90°$$
(a right angle)

(i)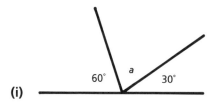

(ii)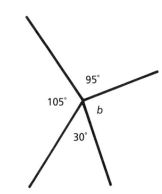

(ii) The angles round a point total
360°, so

$$105° + 95° + b + 30° = 360°$$
$$b = 130°$$
(an obtuse angle)

(iii) The angles round a point total
360°, so

(iii)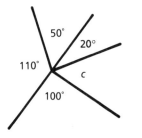

$$100° + 110° + 50° + 20° + c = 360°$$
$$c = 80°$$
(an acute angle)

(iv) The angles round a point total 360°, so

$$30° + 35° + 65° + d = 360°$$
$$d = 230°$$

(a reflex angle)

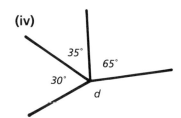

(iv)

(v) $e + 30° = 180°$ (on a straight line)
$e = 150°$ (an obtuse angle)
$f = 30°$ (opposite angles)
(an acute angle)
$g = 150°$ (opposite e)
(an obtuse angle)

(v)

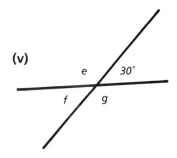

(vi) $h + 125° = 180°$ (on a straight line)
$h = 55°$ (acute angle)
$j = 125°$ (opposite angles)
(obtuse angle)
$k = 55°$ (similar place to h)
(or corresponding angles)
(acute angle)
$l = 125°$ (corresponding to 125°)
(obtuse angle)

(vi)

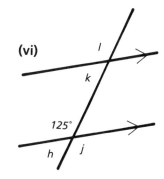

2ª Draw the locus of all points 2 cm from a line segment of length 5 cm. Calculate its length.

Solution

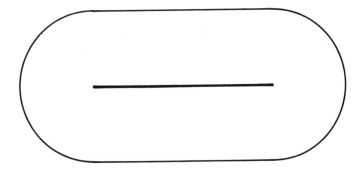

The length of the locus $= 5 + 5 + 2 \times$ length of the semicircle of radius 2 cm
$= 10 + 2\pi2$
$= 22.6$ cm (to 1 d.p.)

b A goat is tethered on a lawn to a point X by a thin chain which is 7 m long. There is a high wall 5 m long as shown in the diagram. Make a scale drawing of the situation and shade in the area of the grass the goat can eat.

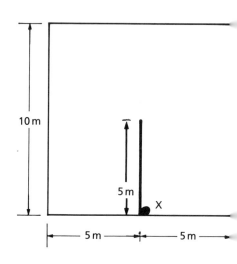

Solution

The scale is 1 cm represents 1 m – from X the goat can go out until the chain is taut; it can then follow an arc until it reaches A. At A the chain is alongside the wall and this restricts any further movement left, so the goat can now follow a circle whose centre is the end of the wall and radius 2 m. The shaded area represents all the points which the goat can reach.

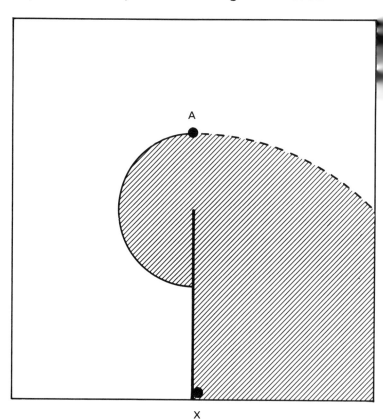

c A square rolls along a line. What is the locus of one corner of the square?

Solution

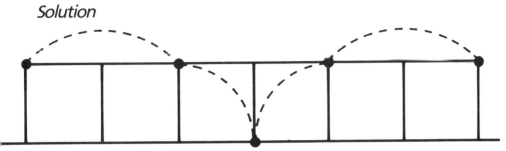

As the square rolls, it rolls around a corner and turns through 90°. The corner then follows a quarter circle each time, sometimes of radius the diagonal of the square and sometimes of radius the side of the square.

'Take note of the rule that determines how the line moves – sketch a diagram on graph paper if necessary'

Do It Yourself

1 Find the angles marked in the following diagrams:

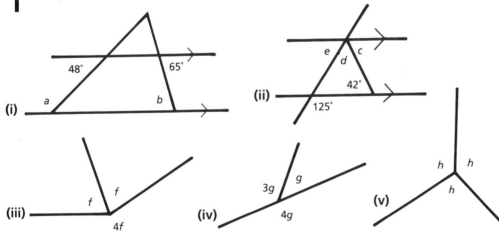

2 a A ship is sailing due west at 10 miles/hour. An enemy gun site with a range of 3 miles is 5 miles west and 2 miles north of the ship. Draw a scale drawing, using 1 cm to represent 1 mile, to show the ship's course and the region in which it is in range of the gun. For how long is the ship in danger?

b A ladder of length 20 ft is placed on horizontal ground against a vertical wall. The bottom of the ladder slips away from the wall. Draw a scale diagram of the situation putting in the ladder in five positions. Sketch the locus of the mid-point of the ladder as it slips down.

12 Shapes and Trigonometry

Things You Need to Know

1 There are many types of triangle:

(i) A **scalene** triangle has no sides the same length.

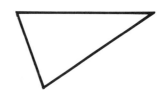

(ii) An **acute-angled** triangle has all its angles less than 90°.

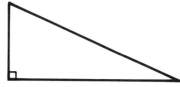

(iii) A **right-angled** triangle has one angle equal to 90°.

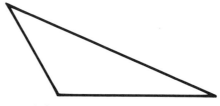

(iv) An **obtuse-angled** triangle has an angle greater than 90°.

(v) An **equilateral** triangle has all sides the same length and all its angles are 60°.

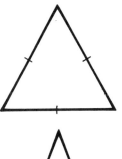

(vi) An **isosceles** triangle has one pair of equal sides, and the angles opposite the equal sides are equal to each other.

In any triangle the angles total 180°.

> *'The longest side of any triangle is opposite the largest angle, and the shortest side is opposite the smallest angle'*

2 When constructing a triangle it is a good idea to draw a sketch of the required triangle, putting in the measurements/labels that you have been given. You can draw a triangle given:
  (i) the three sides;
  (ii) two sides and the included angle;
  (iii) a side and any two angles (you would work with the angles at the ends of the given side).

3 A quadrilateral is a four-sided shape. There are many different types:

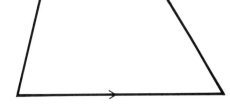

  (i) A **trapezium** has two sides parallel to each other.

  (ii) A **parallelogram** has opposite sides parallel and equal in length.

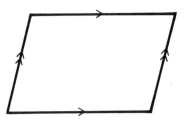

'When sides are the same length they are marked with a small line'

(iii) A **rectangle** has all angles equal to 90°, and opposite sides parallel and equal in length. (You can think of it as a special parallelogram where the angles are all 90°.)

(iv) A **square** is a rectangle with all sides the same length.

(v) A **rhombus** is a parallelogram with all sides the same length (the diagonals cross at 90°). Its opposite angles are equal. Some people think of it as a square 'pushed over'.

(vi) A **kite** has two pairs of adjacent sides equal.

In any quadrilateral the sum of the angles is 360°.

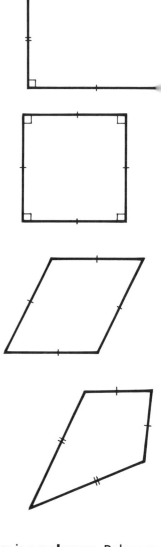

4 The general name for any shape with straight sides is a **polygon**. Polygons are named by the number of sides:

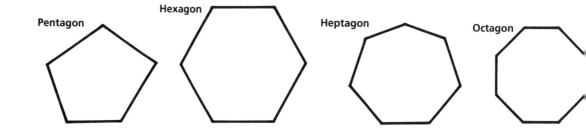

Pentagon

Hexagon

Heptagon

Octagon

If a polygon is described as regular it means that all sides are the same length and the angles are equal to each other.

The sum of the angles of a polygon with *n* sides is given by the formula:

$$180°n - 360°$$

The sum of the exterior angles of any polygon is 360°.

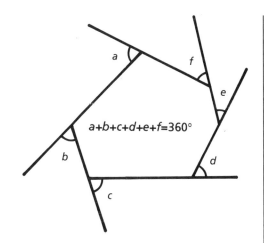

$a+b+c+d+e+f=360°$

The most important shape of all is probably the right-angled triangle. Pythagoras' theorem gives a rule connecting the three sides of a right-angled triangle.

Calling side BC *a* (it is opposite angle A), side AC *b* and side AB *c*, the theorem states that

$$a^2 = b^2 + c^2$$

The best known right-angled triangles have:

  sides 3 units and 4 units, and hypotenuse 5 units
  sides 5 units and 12 units, and hypotenuse 13 units

'The hypotenuse is the side opposite the right angle'

Right-angled triangles also have rules connecting the angles and the sides. Remember that the side opposite the right angle is the hypotenuse. If we call the side next to the given angle the adjacent side, and the other side the opposite side, then we can find three relationships between sides and angles in right-angled triangles. These are the trigonometric ratios: sine (sin), cosine (cos) and tangent (tan) of an angle.

$$\sin = \frac{\text{opposite}}{\text{hypotenuse}} = \frac{O}{H}$$

$$\cos = \frac{\text{adjacent}}{\text{hypotenuse}} = \frac{A}{H}$$

$$\tan = \frac{\text{opposite}}{\text{adjacent}} = \frac{O}{A}$$

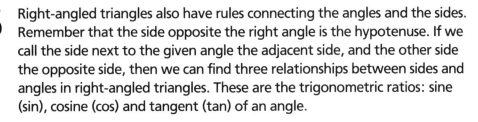

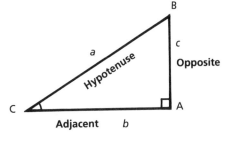

'One way to remember the connection is the nonsense word SOHCAHTOA – pronounced 'so-ca-towwa''

$$\sin C = \frac{c}{a} \qquad \cos C = \frac{b}{a} \qquad \tan C = \frac{c}{b}$$

The equations can be rearranged, to give the following:

opposite = hypotenuse × sin
adjacent = hypotenuse × cos
opposite = adjacent × tan

You must ensure that you can use a calculator to find the sin (or cos, or tan) of an angle; and also, if given the sin (or cos or tan) of an angle, to find the angle (use Inv sin, etc). Correct the answer to three s.f. unless told otherwise.

How to Do It

1 Find the angle x in each of the following triangles, and say what sort of triangle it is.

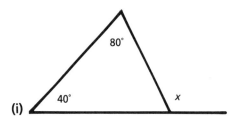 (i)

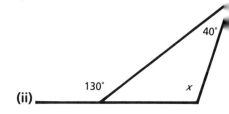 (ii)

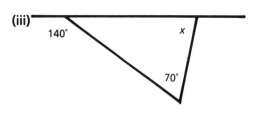 (iii)

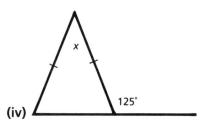 (iv)

Solution

(i)   The other angle of the triangle $= 180° - (80° + 40°)$
$$= 60°$$
$$x + 60° = 180°$$
$$x = 120° \quad \text{(scalene triangle)}$$

(ii) $130° + \text{other angle} = 180°$
         $\text{Other angle} = 50°$
         $50° + 40° + x = 180°$
                      $x = 90°$ (a right-angled triangle)

(iii) $140° + \text{other angle} = 180°$
         $\text{Other angle} = 40°$
         $40° + 70° + x = 180°$
                      $x = 70°$ (an isosceles triangle)

(iv) $125° + \text{other angle} = 180°$
         $\text{Other angle} = 55°$

         Since it is an isosceles triangle other base $= 55°$, so

         $x + 55° + 55° = 180°$
                      $x = 70°$

2 a Draw a triangle with sides of 4 cm, 6 cm and 8 cm.

Solution

Call the triangle ABC and draw a sketch of it first in order to get some idea of how it looks. Try to obtain a reasonable representation of it.

   Now draw it with a pair of compasses. Draw the baseline and measure AB to make it 8 cm. Set the compasses at 4 cm and draw an arc with centre A. Now, set the compasses at 6 cm and draw an arc with centre B; where they cross must be the point C. Draw lines from A to C and from B to C.

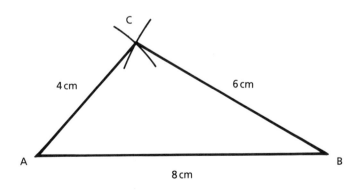

'Make sure your pencil is sharp, your ruler has a good edge and your compasses don't move too easily'

> *'Whenever you are doing any question involving a shape, always draw a sketch of the shape – try to get it to look reasonable'*

b Draw a triangle with sides 9 cm, 4 cm and an included angle of 40°.

Solution

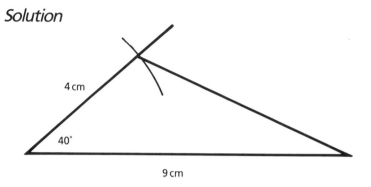

4 cm

40°

9 cm

3 **a** In the diagram ABCD is a parallelogram. Calculate the angles x and y.

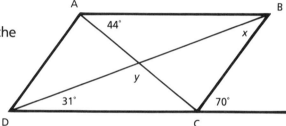

Solution

$$31° + x + \text{angle BCD} = 180°$$
$$\text{Angle BCD} = 180° - 70°$$
$$= 110°$$
$$x = 39°$$
$$\text{Angle ACD} = 44° \quad \text{(parallel lines)}$$
$$31° + 44° + y = 180°$$
$$y = 105°$$

b In a quadrilateral one angle is 60° and the other three angles are all equal to each other. What is the size of the other angles?

Solution

Let a be the size of the other angles:

$$3a + 60° = 360° \quad \text{(angles of a quadrilateral total 360°)}$$
$$3a = 300°$$

So the other angles are each 100°.

¶a The interior angle of a regular polygon is 140°. How many sides has the polygon?

Solution

This is easier if we use the exterior angle, which is

$$180° - 140° = 40°$$

The exterior angles of any polygon total 360° so

$$\text{Number of sides} = \frac{360°}{40°} = 9$$

b A polygon has *n* sides, two of the angles are right angles and each of the other angles is 144°. Calculate the number of sides in the polygon.

Solution

Again, it is easier to use the exterior angles. The exterior angles are 90°, 90° and some number of 36° – these must total 360°:

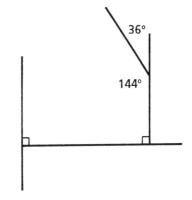

$$90° + 90° + m36° = 360°$$
$$m36° = 180°$$
$$m = 5$$

So the number of sides is 7.

5 For each of the following diagrams find the unknown length marked *d*, correct to three significant figures.

(i)

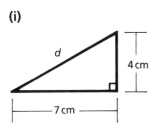

(ii)

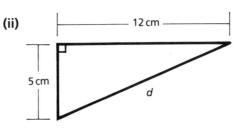

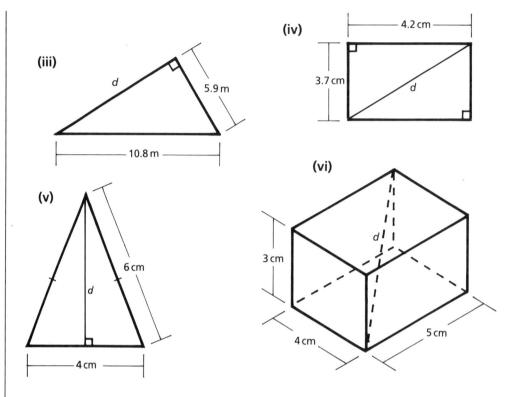

Solution

(i) $d^2 = 7^2 + 4^2$
     $= 65$
     $d = 8.06\,\text{cm}$

(ii) $d^2 = 12^2 + 5^2$
      $= 169$
      $d = 13\ \text{cm}$

(iii) $d^2 + 5.9^2 = 10.8^2$
       $d^2 = 10.8^2 - 5.9^2$
       $= 81.8$
       $d = 9.05\,\text{m}$

(iv) $d^2 = 3.7^2 + 4.2^2$
      $= 31.33$
      $d = 5.60\,\text{cm}$

(v) This is an isosceles triangle. The height bisects the base, so

$d^2 + 2^2 = 6^2$
$d^2 = 32$
$d = 5.66\,\text{cm}$

(vi) All angles at each vertex are right angles, as in a cube. In triangle ABC if AC is called *l*

$$l^2 = 4^2 + 5^2 = 41$$

In triangle ACD

$$d^2 = l^2 + 3^2$$
$$= 41 + 9$$
$$= 50$$
$$d = 7.07 \text{ cm}$$

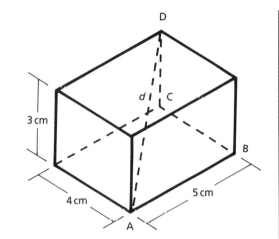

5 a Here is the symmetrical cross-section of an embankment. Calculate the angle *x* made by the sloping sides with the horizontal.

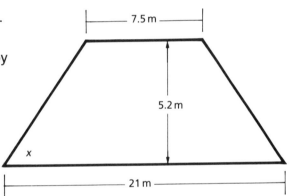

Solution
We need to make a right-angled triangle – drop a line vertically down from a top corner:

$$l + 7.5 + l = 21$$
$$l = 6.75 \text{ m}$$

$$\tan x = \frac{5.2}{6.75}$$

$$x = \tan^{-1}\left(\frac{5.2}{6.75}\right) = 37.6°$$

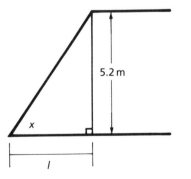

'The trick with this sort of question is to find the right-angled triangles'

b Using a calculator draw up a table showing the sine of angles from 0° to 360° in steps of 30°. Draw a graph to illustrate the results.

Solution

Angle	0	30	60	90	120	150	180	210	240	270	300	330	360
Sine	0	0.5	0.87	1	0.87	0.5	0	−0.5	−0.87	−1	−0.87	−0.5	0

Your calculator must be a scientific one for this. To find the sine of, say, the angle 30°, you need to do the following key presses (the calculator must be in the degrees setting, *not* radians):

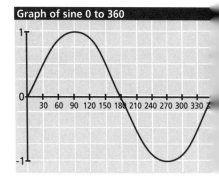

Graph of sine 0 to 360

| 3 | | 0 | | SIN |

The key presses are similar for other trigonometry functions.

If you have been given the sine of an angle and wish to know what the angle is, the following key presses are necessary, assuming you have already entered the sine value:

| INV | | SIN |

Again, the key presses for other trigonometry functions are similar.

c A parallelogram JKLM has an area of 36 cm². The sides are of length 8 cm and 5 cm. Calculate:
   (i) the perpendicular distance between the longer sides;
   (ii) the perpendicular distance between the shorter sides;
   (iii) the acute angle between the long and short sides.

Solution

(i)   Area = $b \times h$

   If the base is the longer side (8 cm) then

   $h = 36 \div 8 = 4.5 \,\text{cm}$

(ii) If the base is the shorter side then

   $h = 36 \div 5 = 7.2 \,\text{cm}$

(i)

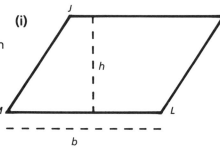

(iii) $\sin x = \dfrac{4.5}{5} = 0.9$

$x = 64.2°$

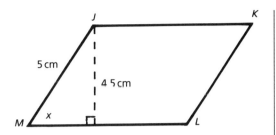

Do It Yourself

1 Find the angles marked with letters:

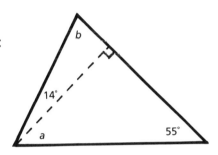

2 Draw a triangle XYZ in which XY is 10 cm long, angle x is 30° and angle y is 60°. Measure the length of XZ and YZ.

3a Find the angles marked with letters:

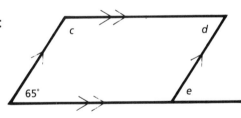

b A quadrilateral has two angles, each of 50°. If the other two angles are equal to each other, what is their size? What type of quadrilateral might it be?

4a A regular polygon has 10 sides. What is the size of:

    (i) an exterior angle;

    (ii) an interior angle.

b If the exterior angle of a regular polygon is 30°:

    (i) how many sides does the polygon have?

    (ii) what is the size of the interior angle?

5 a In the diagram all the equal sides are 12 cm long. Find the lengths of AC and AD.

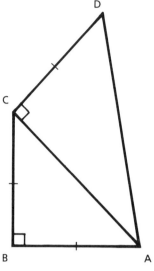

b A gift pack of three bottles is shown in the diagram. The larger bottles have a radius of 12 cm and the smaller bottle has a radius of 4 cm. All the bottles are 20 cm high. By joining the centres of the circles representing the bottles, or otherwise, calculate the dimensions of the gift pack.

'Hint: joining the centres produces what sort of triangle?'

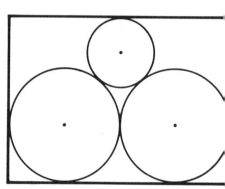

6 a In the diagrams here and opposite, find the angles marked with a letter:

(i)

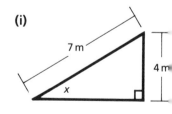

(i)

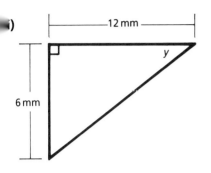

(iii)

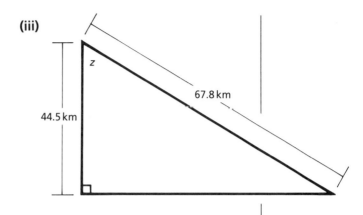

b In the following diagrams, find the sides marked with a letter:

(i)

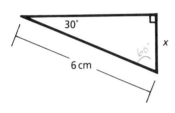

(ii)

(iii)

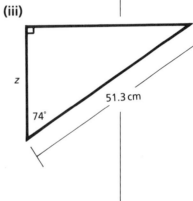

c Points A, B and C lie on level ground such that AB = 20 m and BC = 170 m. At B is a vertical pole which is such that the angle of elevation of T, the top of the pole, from A is 15°. Find the angle of elevation from C.

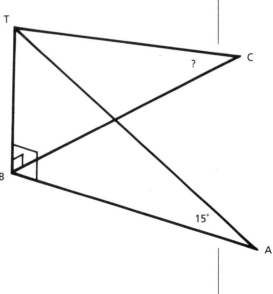

13 | Circles

Things You Need to Know

1 The words you should know are illustrated below:

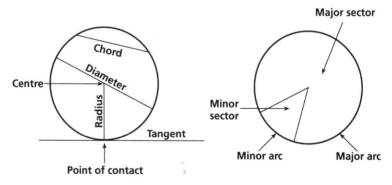

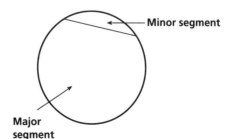

In doing calculations the value of π is often used. This will either be given to you (3.14, or something close to this) or you should use the value given by your calculator. The formulae to be used will be given but you do need to be familiar with them.

Using r for the length of the radius:

Diameter $= 2r$

Circumference $= \pi d$ or $2\pi r$

Area of circle $= \pi r^2$

(π is a number that continues for ever. We normally use 3.14; your calculator will give you a much more accurate figure.)

Angles and circles go together and there are lots of properties of angles that are based around the circle. Here are the ones you should be able to use:

(i) A tangent (a line that touches the circle at one point) is perpendicular to the radius at the point of contact.

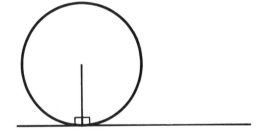

(ii) The angle formed from a diameter to the circumference is always a right angle.

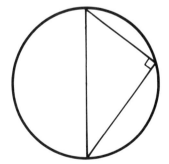

(iii) The angle given at the centre by an arc or chord is twice the angle given at the circumference.

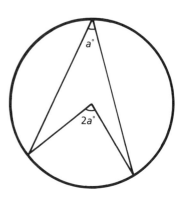

(iv) Angles from the same arc (or arcs of the same length) are equal.

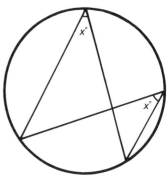

(v) Opposite angles of a quadrilateral in a circle total 180°. This type of quadrilateral is called a cyclic quadrilateral because all four vertices touch the circumference of the circle.

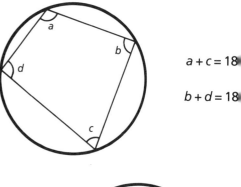

$a + c = 18$

$b + d = 18$

(vi) A line from the centre of the circle to the mid-point of a chord is perpendicular to the chord.

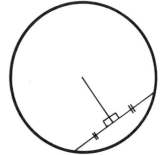

(vii) Equal length chords are the same distance from the centre of the circle.

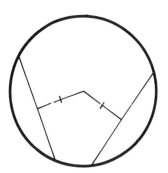

(viii) The two tangents from an external point are the same length, and the angles marked are equal.

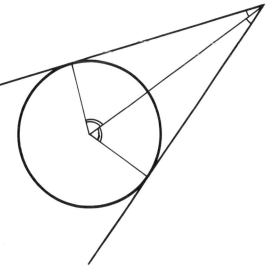

(ix) The angle between a tangent and a chord at the point of contact is equal to the angle in the alternate segment.

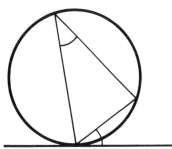

How to Do It

1 On the diagrams various parts of the circle are labelled *a*, *b*, *c* and *d*. What are the correct labels for *a*, *b*, *c* and *d*?

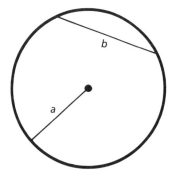 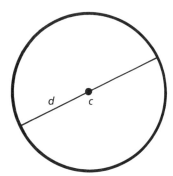

Solution

    a is the radius   *b* is a chord   *c* is the centre   *d* is a diameter

2a A circular running track has a radius of 40 m. What is the distance round the track? What area of grass is inside the track?

Solution

$$\text{Distance round track} = \text{circumference of circle}$$
$$= 2 \times \pi \times 40$$
$$= 251 \text{ m} \quad \text{(to 3 s.f.)}$$

$$\text{Area inside track} = \pi \times 40^2$$
$$= 5030 \text{ m}^2 \quad \text{(to 3 s.f.)}$$

b A tray of length 45 cm and width 55 cm has rounded corners of radius 2.5 cm. What is the perimeter of the tray and what area does it cover?

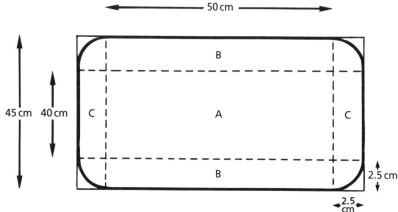

Solution

Perimeter $= 2 \times 40 + 2 \times 50 + 4 \times$ distance round quarter circles

$\qquad = 180 + 2 \times \pi \times 2.5$

$\qquad = 196$ cm   (to 3 s.f.)

Area $= A + 2B + 2C +$ area of 4 quarter circles

$\qquad = 40 \times 50 + 2 \times (40 \times 2.5) + 2 \times (50 \times 2.5) + \pi \times 2.5^2$

$\qquad = 2470$ cm²

3a Find the lettered angles in the following diagrams – O denotes the centre of the circle.

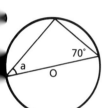
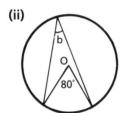
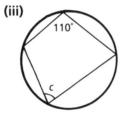
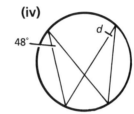

Solution

(i) $a = 20°$ as the other angle is $90°$ (angle in a semicircle)

(ii) $b = \frac{1}{2}$ of $80° = 40°$

(iii) $c = 180° - 110°$ (opposite angles of cyclic quadrilateral total $180°$)

$\qquad = 70°$

(iv) $d = 48°$ (standing on same arc as other $48°$ angle)

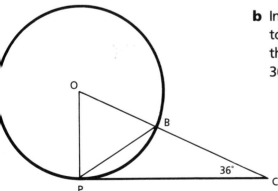

b In the diagram PC is a tangent to the circle centre O. OC cuts the circle at B. If angle OCP is $36°$, find angles POC and OPB.

Solution

OP is a radius, PC is a tangent, hence they are at right angles. Thus

$$\text{angle POC} = 180° - 90° - 36° = 54°$$

OP and OB are both radii – hence equal in length, making OPB an isosceles triangle – so angles OPB and OBP are equal. Thus

$$\text{angle OPB} = \tfrac{1}{2}(180° - 54°) = 63°$$

c Find the marked angles in the following diagrams:

(i)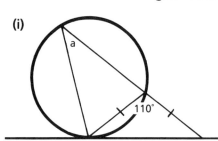

(ii)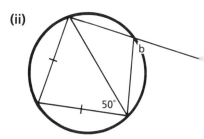

Solution

Firstly label some of the other angles:

(i) $\quad x + y + 110° = 180°$

but $x = y$ (an isosceles triangle), so

$$x = 35°$$

also

$a = x$ (angle between chord and tangent equals angle in alternate segment)

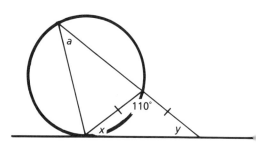

(ii) $y = 50°$ (angle in an isosceles triangle)

so

$$x + 50° + 50° = 180°$$
$$x = 80°$$
$$x + z = 180° \quad \text{(opposite angles}$$
$$\text{of cyclic quadrilateral)}$$
$$z = 100°$$

so

$$b - 80° \quad \text{(angles on a straight line)}$$

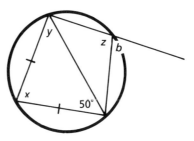

Do It Yourself

Remember: the diagrams shown below are not accurate scale drawings; they are there to help you 'picture' the situations.

1 On a diagram, or diagrams, of a circle mark in and label the following parts:

centre, chord, circumference, diameter, major arc,
minor segment, tangent

2a The hour hand of a clock is 2.75 cm long. How far does it travel in six hours?

b If the total distance round a circular bowl is 28 cm, find the radius of the bowl.

c A circular race track has an inner radius of 45 m and an outer radius of 50 m. What is the difference in length in running one lap on the outer edge compared to one lap on the inner edge?

d A piece of metal 125 mm square has a circle of diameter 75 mm cut out of it. What is the area of metal left?

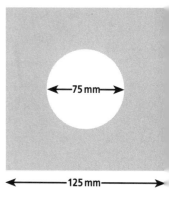

e A piece of metal has the cross-section shown in the diagram. Calculate the area of the cross-section.

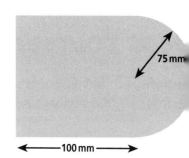

3a The diagram shows a quadrilateral drawn round a circle. Show that
AB + CD = BC + AD.
(*Hint:* think carefully about what each line is as far as the circle is concerned.)

b A circle is drawn inside a triangle so that the sides of the triangle are tangents of the circle. The triangle formed by the points of contact has angles of 55°, 63° and 62°. Find the angles of the original triangle.

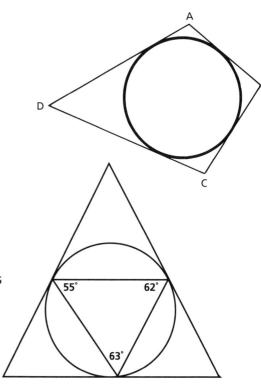

Transformations

Things You Need to Know

1 A shape has **line symmetry** if it is possible to place a straight line such that one side is a reflection of the other. Sometimes a shape may have more than one line, or axis, of symmetry as shown below right.

With a three-dimensional object we have **planes of symmetry**. Imagine a teapot if it were cut straight down through the handle and the spout: we would get two halves which were opposites, like in a mirror.

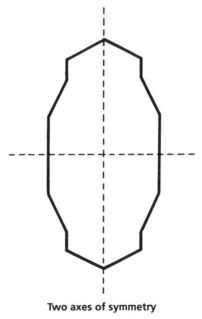

Two axes of symmetry

'This is sometimes referred to as lateral inversion'

2 A shape is reflected in a **mirror line**. Straight lines joining corresponding points will cross the mirror line at right angles and be bisected by it. The size of the reflected shape is the same as the original, but the direction of the shape is opposite, like in a mirror.

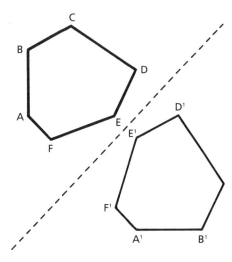

3 When a shape is turned around some point, this transformation is called a **rotation**. With a rotation there has to be a centre of rotation, an angle of rotation and a direction of rotation – either clockwise (also known as negative) or anticlockwise (also known as positive).

   The rotated image is identical to the original in all respects.

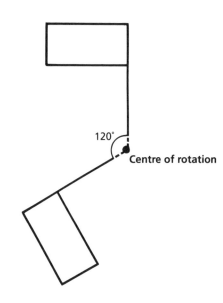

4 A shape has **rotational symmetry** if it can be turned around some point so that it fits back to the original shape with a turn of less than 360°. The order of rotational symmetry is the number of times this can be done as the shape is rotated through 360°.

Order 3

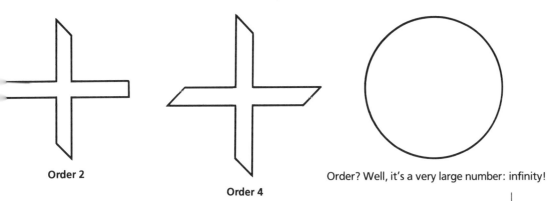

Order 2

Order 4

Order? Well, it's a very large number: infinity!

5 A **translation** moves the position of the shape, without any turning or twisting – the shape simply 'slides' to the new position. It can be described in words ('move it along 4 to the right and 2 upwards') or it can be given as a vector movement (see Section 10). The translated shape is identical to the original.

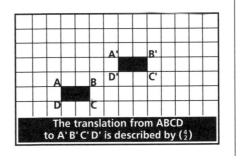

The translation from ABCD to A'B'C'D' is described by $\binom{4}{2}$

'*Scale factor is image length divided by object length*'

6 When the size of a shape is changed but its actual shape stays the same, this is termed an **enlargement**. An enlargement must have a centre of enlargement and an enlargement factor, or **scale factor**. If this is greater than 1 then the image produced will be larger than the original; however, if the enlargement factor is between 0 and 1 then the image produced will be smaller than the original.

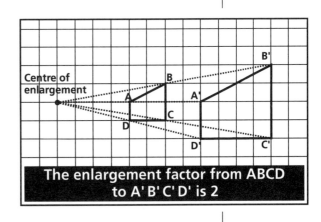

Centre of enlargement

The enlargement factor from ABCD to A'B'C'D' is 2

7 Transformations can be combined as follows:

Rotation then rotation = rotation
Translation then translation = translation
Reflection then reflection = rotation (if mirror lines not parallel)
Reflection then reflection = translation (if mirror lines are parallel)

8 A transformation can be represented by a matrix. A matrix is just a block of numbers. Each point's coordinates are written as a vertical pair and multiplied by the matrix:

$$\begin{pmatrix} 1 & 2 \\ 3 & 4 \end{pmatrix} \begin{pmatrix} -5 \\ 6 \end{pmatrix} = \begin{pmatrix} 1 \times -5 + 2 \times 6 \\ 3 \times -5 + 4 \times 6 \end{pmatrix} = \begin{pmatrix} 7 \\ 9 \end{pmatrix}$$

The matrix above represents a transformation that takes the point $(-5, 6)$ to the point $(7, 9)$. If there is more than one point to be transformed, write all the coordinates in one block and multiply. Consider the triangle $(0, 1)$, $(3, 2)$, $(4, 6)$. This becomes a block with two rows and three columns:

$$\begin{pmatrix} 1 & 2 \\ 3 & 4 \end{pmatrix} \begin{pmatrix} 0 & 3 & 4 \\ 1 & 2 & 6 \end{pmatrix} = \begin{pmatrix} 2 & 7 & 16 \\ 4 & 17 & 36 \end{pmatrix}$$

The triangle is transformed to $(2, 4)$, $(7, 17)$ and $(16, 36)$.

The standard transformation matrices are:

$$\begin{pmatrix} 0 & 1 \\ -1 & 0 \end{pmatrix} \text{ and } \begin{pmatrix} 0 & -1 \\ 1 & 0 \end{pmatrix}$$

These represent *rotations* about the origin of 90° clockwise and anticlockwise.

$$\begin{pmatrix} 1 & 0 \\ 0 & -1 \end{pmatrix}, \begin{pmatrix} -1 & 0 \\ 0 & 1 \end{pmatrix} \text{ and } \begin{pmatrix} 0 & 1 \\ 1 & 0 \end{pmatrix}$$

These represent *reflections* in the x-axis, the y-axis and the line $y = x$ respectively.

$$\begin{pmatrix} k & 0 \\ 0 & k \end{pmatrix}$$

This represents an *enlargement* of scale factor k, centred about the origin.

How to Do It

1 a Complete the following shapes, where the dotted line (or lines) represents a line (or lines) of symmetry:

(i)   (ii)   (iii)

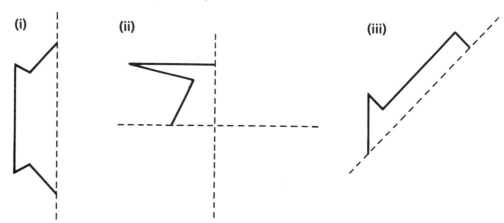

Solution

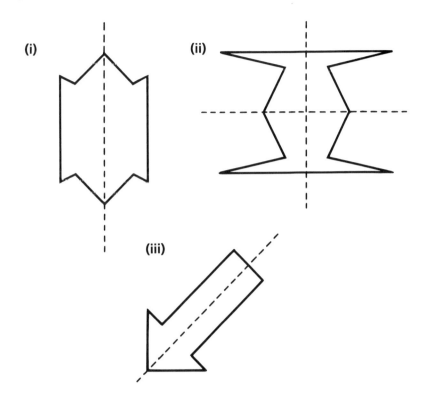

(i)

(ii)

(iii)

b The diagrams below show a square, a rhombus, an isosceles trapezium (sloping sides the same length), an equilateral triangle, an isosceles triangle and a regular hexagon. Make a copy of each shape and on it draw all the axes of symmetry.

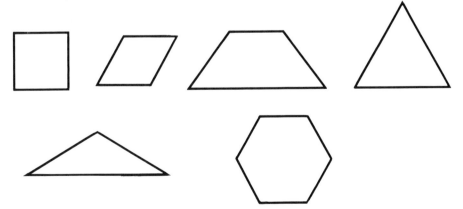

Solution

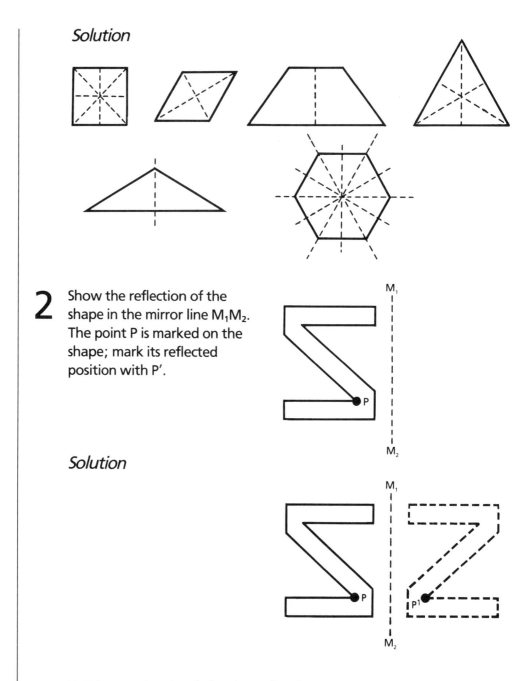

2 Show the reflection of the shape in the mirror line M_1M_2. The point P is marked on the shape; mark its reflected position with P′.

Solution

3 XYZ has vertices (2, 0), (2, 2) and (6, 0), respectively. Draw the image X′Y′Z′ of XYZ after it has been rotated 90° clockwise about the origin.

Solution

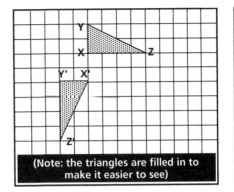

(Note: the triangles are filled in to make it easier to see)

4 Which of the following shapes have rotational symmetry? Make a sketch of those that do, show the centre of rotation and give the order of symmetry.

Solution

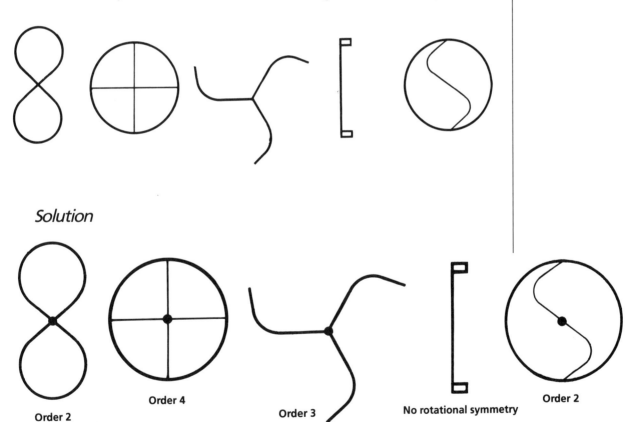

Order 2

Order 4

Order 3

No rotational symmetry

Order 2

5 The drawing shows a 4 × 6 lettered grid.

(i) What translation takes G to L?

(ii) What translation takes T to K?

(iii) A translation takes S to P. Where does this same translation take G? What was taken to R by this translation?

A	B	C	D	E	F
G	H	I	J	K	L
M	N	O	P	Q	R
S	T	U	V	W	X

Solution

(i) 5 to the right;   (ii) 3 right and 2 up;   (iii) G goes to D. It must have started at U.

6 The letter F is shown on the grid. Enlarge it by a factor of 2 using the point P as the centre of enlargement.

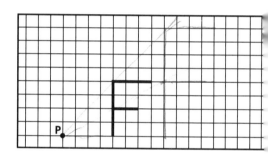

Solution

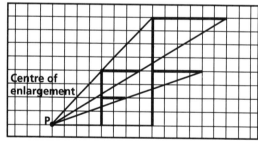

Centre of enlargement

P

7 The triangle ABC with vertices A(1, 1), B(3, 2) and C(4, 0) is reflected in the line $x = 1$ and this is then reflected in the line $x = 2$. Find the single translation that is equivalent to the two reflections.

Solution

The overall effect is a translation 2 units to the right.

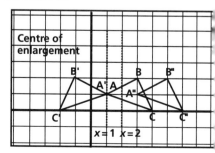

8 The triangle T has been drawn on a grid and is transformed by the matrix **M** to give the triangle T'.

$$\mathbf{M} = \begin{pmatrix} -1 & 0 \\ 0 & -1 \end{pmatrix}$$

(i) Work out the coordinates of T'
(ii) On the grid draw and label T'
(iii) Describe the single transformation represented by **M**.

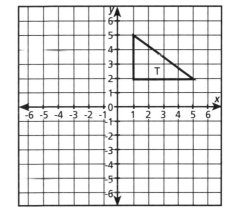

Solution

(i) $\begin{pmatrix} -1 & 0 \\ 0 & -1 \end{pmatrix} \begin{pmatrix} 1 & 1 & 5 \\ 2 & 5 & 2 \end{pmatrix} = \begin{pmatrix} -1 & -1 & -5 \\ -2 & -5 & -2 \end{pmatrix}$

So, the coordinates of T' are $(-1, -2)$, $(-1, -5)$ and $(-5, -2)$

(ii)

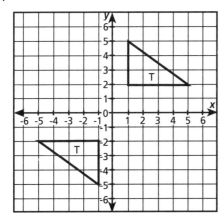

(iii) **M** represents a rotation of 180° about the origin.

Do It Yourself

1 Draw the image of each of the given shapes when reflected in the dotted line.

(i) (ii) (iii)

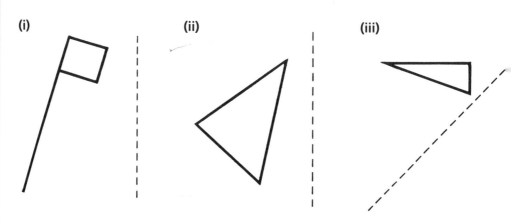

2 Mark the mirror line for each of the following:

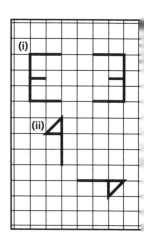

3 The triangle ABC has vertices (2, 1), (3, 3) and (6, 0) respectively. Draw the image A'B'C' of ABC after it has been rotated 90° clockwise about C. Also draw the image A''B''C'' of A'B'C' after it has been rotated 90° about A'.

4 For each of the following draw a shape which has rotational symmetry of:
(i) order 6   (ii) order 2   (iii) order 3   (iv) order 0

5

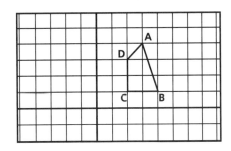

(i) The shape ABCD shown in the diagram is translated

$$\begin{pmatrix} 3 \\ -2 \end{pmatrix}$$

What are the coordinates of A′B′C′D′?

(ii) The shape ABCD is the result of a translation; the original position of B was the origin. What were the original coordinates of ABCD and what was the translation?

6

Enlarge each of the following shapes by the factor given using C as the centre of enlargement:

(i)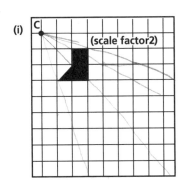
(scale factor 2)

(ii)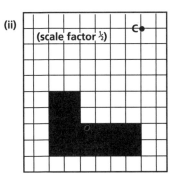
(scale factor ½)

7
The triangle XYZ has vertices (0, 0), (3, 0) and (3, 2) respectively. It is first reflected in the line $x = 0$ to give X′Y′Z′ and this is then reflected in the line $y = 0$ to give X″Y″Z″. Find the single transformation that would go from XYZ to X″Y″Z″.

8
The square (0, 0), (0, 2), (2, 2) and (2, 0) is transformed by the matrix **X** to the points (0, 0), (2, 4), (6, 10) and (4, 6). Find the matrix **X**.

'Do one trans-formation to produce your first image, then do the next trans-formation on that image'

15 | Areas and Volumes

Things You Need to Know

1 You should be able to name the following shapes:

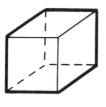

Cube

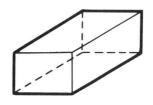

Cuboid

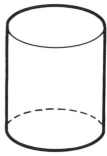

Cylinder

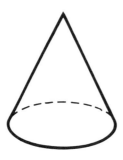

Cone

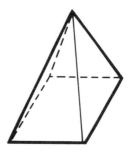

Square pyramid

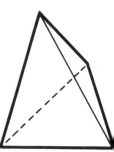

Triangular Pyramid
(or tetrahedron)

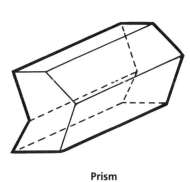

Prism

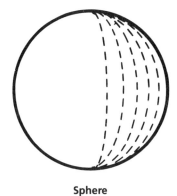

Sphere

2 A **net** is a flat shape that can be folded into the shape of a three-dimensional object – here is a net for a cuboid (try to imagine how it folds).

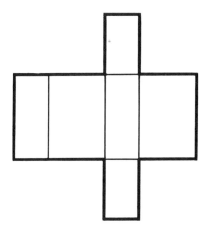

3 The area of a surface can be quite important. We measure the area of a surface in 'square centimetres' (cm²). For the basic shapes there are standard formulae that are used:

Area of rectangle is
length x breadth
(or $A = l \times b$)

l

b

Area of parallelogram is
height x breadth
(or $A = h \times b$)

h

b

'*Square centimetres are not the same as centimetres squared*'

131

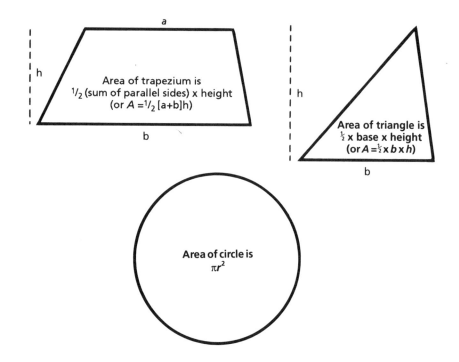

Area of trapezium is
$1/2$ (sum of parallel sides) x height
(or $A = 1/2 [a+b]h$)

Area of triangle is
$\frac{1}{2}$ x base x height
(or $A = \frac{1}{2} x b x h$)

Area of circle is
πr^2

4   The volume of a three-dimensional shape is measured in 'cubic centimetres' (cm³). For the basic objects there are standard formulae for the volume:

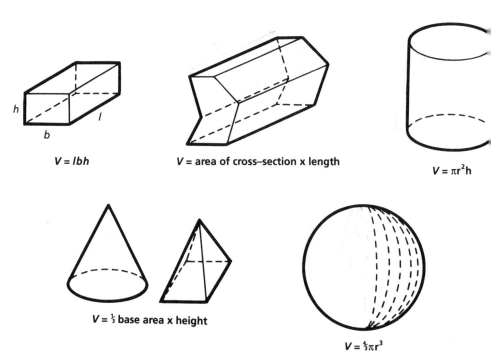

$V = lbh$

$V =$ area of cross–section x length

$V = \pi r^2 h$

$V = \frac{1}{3}$ base area x height

$V = \frac{4}{3} \pi r^3$

How to Do It

1 Surfaces can be either flat or curved. For each of the following shapes say how many flat surfaces and how many curved surfaces it has:

(i) a cube   (ii) a cylinder

(iii) a square pyramid   (iv) a cone

Solution

(i) A cube has six flat surfaces and no curved surfaces.

(ii) A cylinder has two flat surfaces and one curved surface.

(iii) A square pyramid has five flat surfaces and no curved surfaces.

(iv) A cone has one flat surface and one curved surface.

2 Each of the following is a net of a three-dimensional object. For each net state the name of the object it forms:

(i)   **(ii)**

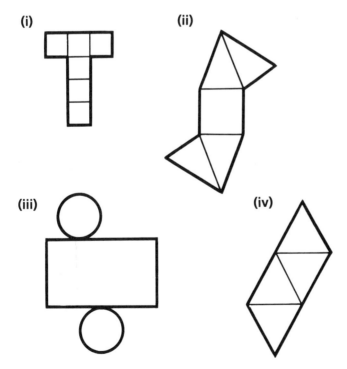

(iii)   **(iv)**

Solution

(i) a cube   (ii) a square pyramid

(iii) a cylinder   (iv) a triangular pyramid (or tetrahedron)

3

a A photograph, 20 cm by 14 cm, is placed in a frame which is 22 cm by 16 cm. What is the area of the border?

Solution

Area of frame $= 16 \times 22$ cm$^2 = 352$ cm^2
Area of photo $= 20 \times 14$ cm$^2 = 280$ cm^2
Area of border $= 352 - 280$ cm$^2 = 72$ cm^2

b A circular picture of radius 7 cm is put into the frame in question 3(a) above. What is the area of the border now?

Solution

Area of frame $= 352$ cm^2
Area of picture $= \pi \times 7^2$ cm^2
$\qquad\qquad\qquad = 154$ cm^2 (to 3 s.f.)
Area of border $= 352 - 154$ cm$^2 = 198$ cm^2

c The parallelogram ABCD has its vertices at (1, 1), (2, 3), (5, 3) and (4, 1). Find its area.

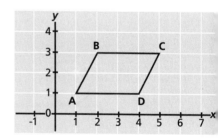

Solution

Area of parallelogram $=$ base $\times$ perpendicular height

Base $= 3$ units, height $= 2$ units, so

$\qquad$ Area $= 6$ units^2

4a The surface of a pond is a square of side 150 cm. During a very cold spell the pond froze to a depth of 2.5 cm. Find the mass of the ice, given that the density of ice is 0.9 g/cm³.

Solution

$$\text{Volume of ice} = 150 \times 150 \times 2.5 \text{ cm}^3$$
$$= 56\,250 \text{ cm}^3$$
$$\text{Mass of the ice} = 0.9 \times 56\,250 \text{ g}$$
$$= 50\,625 \text{ g}$$
$$= 50.625 \text{ kg}$$

b An ingot of steel whose volume is 2 m³ is rolled to a plate 15 mm thick and 1.75 m wide. Find the length of the steel in metres.

Solution

Volume of the ingot $= 2$ m³ so volume of the plate $= 2$ m³. Changing the measurements of the plate so that they are in metres:

$$2 = 1.75 \times 0.015 \times \text{length of plate}$$
$$\text{Length of plate} = \frac{2}{0.02625}$$
$$= 76.2 \text{ m} \quad \text{(to 3 s.f.)}$$

Do It Yourself

1 Imagine you are on the telephone to someone who does not know about three-dimensional shapes. Using not more than three sentences for each, how would you describe:
 (i) a cube
 (ii) a cylinder
 (iii) a prism
 (iv) a sphere

2 What shape can be made from the following nets:

(i) (ii) (iii) (iv)

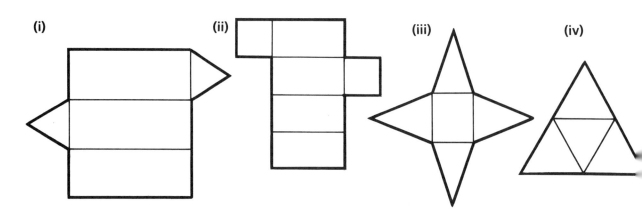

3a The diagram shows a 4 cm square with a diagonal band which is 1.5 cm from the corners. Find

(i) the perimeter of the square;
(ii) the unshaded area;
(iii) the area of the shaded band;
(iv) the width of the band.

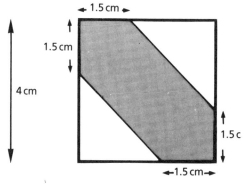

b A metal disc with radius 5 cm comes to rest with its centre 3 cm from the edge of the table. Calculate the area of the disc on the table.

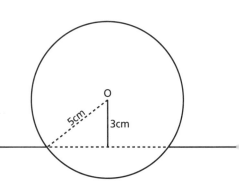

c What is the surface area of a solid cube whose volume is 64 cm³?

d A triangle has sides of 3 cm, 4 cm and 5 cm. Show that it is a right-angled triangle and hence calculate its area.

a A concrete gully is to be made in the shape indicated in the diagram. Calculate:

    (i) the cross-sectional area;
    (ii) the volume of the gully;
    (iii) the mass of the gully if
        1 cm³ of concrete has a
        mass of 6 g.

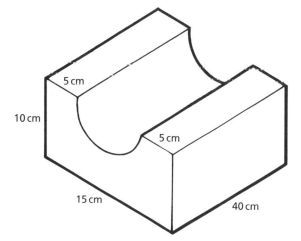

b A container consists of a cylinder of radius 10 cm and height 15 cm, with a conical top of height 25 cm. What is its volume?.

> *'A complex shape can often be broken up into simple shapes – so add their areas to give that of the complex shape. Don't forget to subtract for any holes'*

16 | **Algebra**

Things You Need to Know

1 Only like terms can be added/subtracted. For example:

$2x + 5x$ can be combined to become $7x$.

Similarly, $9xy - 4xy$ can be written as $5xy$.

But $10a^2b + 7ab^2$ is just that; we *cannot* add them because a^2b and ab^2 are *unlike* terms.

The multiplication sign ($\times$) can easily be mistaken for the letter 'x' so we normally would not write the multiplication sign – this means that if there are two things without a sign between them then they are being multiplied. So the multiplication of terms is fairly straightforward, e.g.

$8a^3b^2 \times 2a^2b = 8a^3b^2 2a^2b = 16a^5b^3$

Dividing terms is simply a matter of putting them down as a fraction and cancelling:

$$\frac{8a^3b^2}{2a^2b^3} = \frac{4a}{b}$$

Brackets are used as a way of keeping terms together so that these terms are treated like a single thing. For example, 'think of a number, double it, add 10 and then halve the result' would be written as:

$\frac{1}{2}(2n + 10)$

When removing brackets, remember that the term before the bracket multiplies *everything* inside the bracket:

$5(2x - 3y) = 10x - 15y$

When we have two pairs of brackets such as:

$(2a + 3b)(4a - 5b)$

we can produce a similar diagram, where each term in the first pair of brackets multiplies each term in the second pair of brackets:

$$(2a + 3b)(4a - 5b) = 8a^2 - 10ab + 12ab - 15b^2$$
$$= 8a^2 + 2ab - 15b^2$$

The process of multiplying out brackets is known as **expanding** them.

When an equation contains just one unknown quantity – let's call it n – and does not contain n^2 or n^3 or higher powers, then the equation is called a **simple equation**. It can also be called a **linear equation** because, when drawn as a graph, it would produce a straight line.

$$2n + 12 = 20$$
$$2n + 12 - 12 = 20 - 12$$
$$2n = 8$$
$$n = 4$$

The aim with equations is to rearrange them so that the terms involving the letter are on one side and the numbers are on the other.

'Linear equations have only a letter like x, *and no squares or cubes'*

3 **Inequalities** deal with a possible range of values for the unknown. We use the following symbols:

$<$ means 'less than'   e.g. $a < 9$
$\leqslant$ means 'less than or equal to'   e.g. $b \leqslant 6$
$>$ means 'greater than'   e.g. $c > 4$
$\geqslant$ means 'greater than or equal to'   e.g. $d \geqslant 12$

All of the examples are illustrated with reference to the number line:

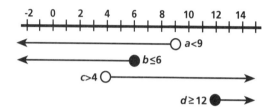

The way to solve an inequality is *almost* always the same as if it were an equation (i.e. do the same to both sides of the inequality sign). The exception is when you multiply or divide by a negative value. Consider the following example:

Obviously, $7 > -3$.
But if we multiply both sides by -2 it gives

$-14 > 6$ (not correct)

The only way to make it correct is to turn round the sign:

$-14 < 6$

From this simple example we can see that when we multiply or divide an inequality by a negative value, we must also turn round the inequality sign.
     Now consider if you were asked to think of a number, then double it and add 12, and you said that your answer was greater than 30, but less than 40. There are a range of possible numbers you might have thought of which could be written as follows:

$2n + 12 > 30$ $2n + 12 < 40$
$2n > 30 - 12$ $2n < 40 - 12$
$2n > 18$ $2n < 28$
$n > 9$ $n < 14$

So *n* is between 9 and 14:

thus $9 < n < 14$

(If only whole numbers are allowed, *n* is either 10, 11, 12 or 13.)
We can extend this and use graphs to help solve inequalities that use two variables, e.g.

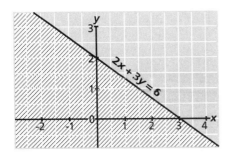

We use the convention that a continuous line may be used if values on that line satisfy the inequality. A broken line is used if the values do not satisfy the inequality. Shade the side of the line that is required. As you work through, use different shadings for each of the inequalities.

4 **Factorising** an expression is the exact opposite of removing, or expanding, brackets – in other words, you ask yourself whether the expression can be split into expressions that multiply together to make the whole. An illustration of the process is

$7ry - 21sy = 7y(r - 3s)$ and $6x^2 - 5x + 3 = (3x - 3)(x - 1)$

The *difference of two squares* can always be factorised:

$a^2 - b^2 = (a - b)(a + b)$

You may meet the term *completing the square*. This involves either adding a number to, or subtracting it from, the expression so that the part involving the letters becomes a square term:

$$x^2 + 6x - 5 = x^2 + 6x \qquad - 5$$
$$= x^2 + 6x + 9 \quad - 5 - 9$$
$$= (x + 3)^2 - 14$$

5 An equation involving a square term (and no higher term) is known as a **quadratic equation**. There are five main ways of solving these:

(i) *Factorising* (see above), can sometimes be used, because of the fact that if two numbers multiply to give zero then either one or the other must be zero. See how this works in the following example:

$$x^2 - 3x = -2$$
$$x^2 - 3x + 2 = 0$$
$$(x-2)(x-1) = 0$$

so either

$$x - 2 = 0$$
$$x = 2$$

or

$$x - 1 = 0$$
$$x = 1$$

You will see by substituting back in the original equation that either $x = 2$ or $x = 1$ satisfies the equation.

(ii) Sometimes it won't factorise, so we 'make it factorise' by completing the square (see previous page) as in the following example:

$$x^2 - 10x + 13 = 0$$
$$x^2 - 10x = -13$$
$$x^2 - 10x + 25 = 25 - 13$$
$$(x-5)^2 = 12$$
$$(x-5) = \pm\sqrt{12}$$
$$x - 5 = \pm 3.46$$
$$x = 5 + 3.46 \text{ or } 5 - 3.46$$
$$x = 8.46 \text{ or } 1.54$$

(iii) We could use the following *formula* for solving quadratics. Whereas factorising will only solve quadratic equations sometimes, this method always works.

$$x = \frac{-b \pm \sqrt{b^2 - 4ac}}{2a}$$

This uses a and b for the coefficients (or multipliers) of x^2 and x, and uses c for the number. It is derived from the basic quadratic equation

$$ax^2 + bx + c = 0$$

For example, in

$$x^2 - 5x + 2 = 0$$
$$a = 1 \qquad b = -5 \qquad c = 2$$

Substitute these values into the formula.

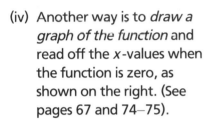

$$x = \frac{-b \pm \sqrt{b^2 - 4ac}}{2a}$$

$$= \frac{-(-5) \pm \sqrt{(-5)^2 - 4 \times 1 \times 2}}{2 \times 1}$$

$$= \frac{5 \pm \sqrt{25 - 8}}{2}$$

$$= \frac{5 \pm \sqrt{17}}{2}$$

$$= 4.56 \text{ or } 0.44$$

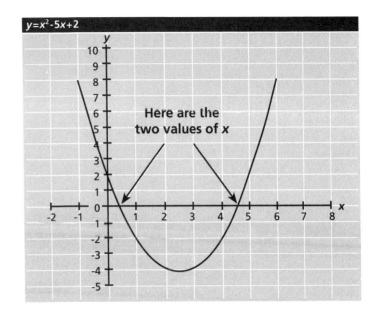

$y = x^2 - 5x + 2$

Here are the two values of x

(iv) Another way is to *draw a graph of the function* and read off the x-values when the function is zero, as shown on the right. (See pages 67 and 74–75).

(v) Guessing the answer, or **trial and improvement**, is also acceptable. Obviously, this doesn't mean making wild guesses. Consider the equation we solved using the formula

$$x^2 - 5x + 2 = 0$$

Let's rewrite it as

$$y = x^2 - 5x + 2 \text{ (and we want to find the } x \text{ that makes } y = 0)$$

Try $x = 0$, $y = 2$ (y is calculated from the x value)
  $x = 1$, $y = -2$

Since y changes from positive to negative as x goes from 0 to 1, there is a solution between these values of x.

Try $x = 0.5$, $y = -0.25$
Try $x = 0.4$, $y = 0.16$

So we know it lies between $x = 0.4$ and $x = 0.5$

Try $x = 0.45$, $y = -0.0475$

So it is less than $x = 0.45$

Try $x = 0.44$, $y = -0.0064$ (very close)

We could go on and try 0.435 and so on until it is accurate enough for what is required.

'This method is much easier with a calculator'

'Don't forget that there is another answer to find as well! The problem with this method is making the first guess'

Another sort of sensible guessing involves using an **iteration formula**. Suppose we have the equation

$$x^2 + 4x - 9 = 0$$

We can rearrange this to give

$$x^2 = \frac{9}{x} - 4$$

If we write this as

$$x_{n+1} = \frac{9}{x_n} - 4$$

we can use a value of x (called x_n in the formula) to generate a better value for x, called x_{n+1}. We can then substitute this better value into the equation to find an even better value, repeating the process until we have a value as accurate as required. In the above equation, $x_0 = 1$, $x_1 = 5$, $x_2 = -2.2$, $x_3 = -8.09$, $x_4 = -5.11$, $x_5 = -5.76$, $x_6 = -5.56$, $x_7 = -5.62$, $x_8 = -5.60$, $x_9 = -5.61$, and so on.

The iteration formula 'homes in', or **converges**, on the solution. If the formula finds the solution within a few attempts, we say it converges fast. Otherwise, we say it converges slowly.

This is an ideal method for use with a computer or calculator.

6 **Simultaneous equations** are equations with *two* unknowns. In order to find the values of the two unknowns, two separate equations are necessary, and the values of the two unknowns will satisfy both equations simultaneously. To find the values, you attempt to eliminate one of the unknowns by adding, subtracting, multiplying or dividing the equations in order to form just one equation. Then, once one unknown has been found, you can substitute its value in one of the original equations and solve for the other unknown.

$$2x - 3y = 8 \qquad \text{(call this equation A)}$$
$$3x + y = 1 \qquad \text{(call this equation B)}$$

Multiply equation B by 3:

$$9x + 3y = 3 \qquad \text{(call this equation C)}$$

Now add equation A and equation B:

$$2x-3y = 8$$
$$9x+3y = 3$$
$$11x = 11$$
$$x = 1$$

Now substitute 1 for x in equation A:

$$2(1)-3y = 8$$
$$2-3y = 8$$
$$-3y = 6$$
$$y = -2$$

Another method of solving simultaneous equations is to draw the graphs of the two equations and see where they cross (see page 67).

7 Algebra is a type of mathematical shorthand, using letters to represent numbers. It is often used as a way of describing a rule, or formula, for finding the value for something (like the area of a circle, or volume of a pyramid). It is also used for problem-solving. You should be able to express a simple mathematical problem as an equation, solve the equation and then check that the solution(s) are appropriate.

How to Do It

a Simplify the following:

    (i) $5a+3b+2a$ (ii) $6c-3d+4d$
    (iii) $-3r+2s-5r-10s$ (iv) $5b+3c-6b-4c+b$
    (v) $a^2 \times b^2 \times 2a^3$ (vi) $7m^3n^2 \times 3m^4n^3$
    (vii) $15v^4w^3 \div 9v^3w^5$ (viii) $14h^3k^3 \div 7hk^2$

Solution

    (i) $5a+3b+2a = 7a+3b$ (ii) $6c-3d+4d = 6c+d$
    (iii) $-3r+2s-5r-10s = -8r-8s$ (iv) $5b+3c-6b-4c+b = -c$
    (v) $a^2 \times b^2 \times 2a^3 = 2a^5b^2$ (vi) $7m^3n^2 \times 3m^4n^3 = 21m^7n^5$

    (vii) $15v^4w^3 \div 9v^3w^5 = \dfrac{5v}{3w^2}$ (viii) $14h^3k^3 \div 7hk^2 = 2h^2k$

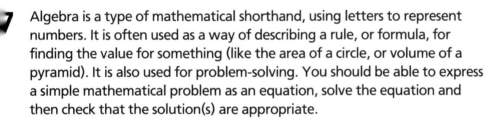

$$-\frac{2\psi \pm \sqrt{\psi^2 - 4\alpha c}}{\alpha c}$$

b Rewrite each of the following formulae to make the given letter the subject:

(i) $a+b = s+t$ (t) (ii) $x^2+y = z$ (x) (iii) $a = \sqrt{\dfrac{b+c}{2b}}$ (b)

Solution

(i) Reverse the order:

$$s+t = a+b$$
$$t = a+b-s$$

(ii) $\quad x^2+y = z$
$$x^2 = z-y$$
$$x = \sqrt{z-y}$$

(iii)
$$a = \sqrt{\dfrac{b+c}{2b}}$$
$$a^2 = \dfrac{b+c}{2b}$$
$$2a^2b = b+c$$
$$2a^2b-b = c$$
$$b(2a^2-1) = c$$
$$b = \dfrac{c}{(2a^2-1)}$$

> *'You must do the same thing to each side of the equation'*

2 Solve each of the following equations:

(i) $6m+11 = 25-m$ (ii) $3(x-1)-4(2x+3) = 20$

(iii) $\dfrac{m}{2}+\dfrac{m}{3}-3 = 2+\dfrac{m}{6}$ (iv) $\dfrac{3-2t}{4} = \dfrac{4-5t}{3}$

Solution

(i) $\quad 6m+11 = 25-m$

Add m to both sides and subtract 11 from both sides:

$$6m+m = 25-11$$
$$7m = 14$$
$$m = 2$$

(ii) $3(x-1)-4(2x+3) = 20$

Remove the brackets first – care with the minus sign!

$$3x-3-8x-12 = 20$$
$$-5x-15 = 20$$

Add 15 to both sides:

$$-5x = 35$$
$$x = -7$$

(iii) $\dfrac{m}{2}+\dfrac{m}{3}-3 = 2+\dfrac{m}{6}$

Multiply both sides by 6:

$$3m+2m-18 = 12+m$$

Rearrange (letters on one side, numbers on the other):

$$4m = 30$$
$$m = 7.5$$

(iv) $\dfrac{3-2t}{4} = \dfrac{4-5t}{3}$

Multiply both sides by 12:

$$3(3-2t) = 4(4-5t)$$
$$9-6t = 16-20t$$
$$14t = 7$$
$$t = 0.5$$

3a Solve the following inequalities and represent each solution on a number line:

   (i) $x+5 > 7$
   (ii) $3x+22 \geqslant 8x-18$
   (iii) $6x+11 \leqslant 25-x$

Solution

(i) $x + 5 > 7$
      $x > 2$

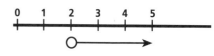

(ii)
      $3x + 22 \geqslant 8x - 18$
      $22 + 18 \geqslant 8x - 3x$
      $30 \geqslant 5x$

   or

      $5x \leqslant 30$
      $x \leqslant 6$

(iii) $6x + 11 \leqslant 25 - x$
       $6x + x \leqslant 25 - 11$
       $7x \leqslant 14$
       $x \leqslant 2$

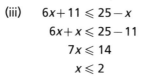

b What are the whole number solutions to the following pairs of inequalities:

   (i) $x < 3$ and $x \geqslant 1$
   (ii) $x < 0$ and $x \geqslant 4$
   (iii) $2x - 3 \leqslant 3$ and $x + 1 \geqslant 2$

Solution

(i) $x < 3$ and $x \geqslant 1$

So x is 1 or 2.

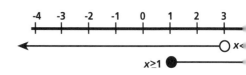

(ii) $x < 0$ and $x \geqslant 4$

There is no solution to this that fits both at the same time.

(iii) $2x - 3 \leqslant 3$ and $x + 1 \geqslant 2$

Rewriting each gives

   $x \leqslant 3$ and $x \geqslant 1$

So x is 1 or 2 or 3.

c Illustrate on a graph the solution of the inequality

$$3y + 6x < 12$$

Solution

If $3y + 6x < 12$ then

$$3y < -6x + 12$$
$$y < -2x + 4$$

So we have to draw the graph of
$y = -2x + 4$, which is a straight line,
and decide which side of the graph is
the side that 'fits' the inequality
we can do this by using any point
but if the graph does not go through
$(0, 0)$ then that is an easy one to test
with:

$$3(0) + 6(0) < 12 \quad \text{true}$$

so $(0, 0)$ *is* on the side we require.

d At Christmas Elisa is given £6.00 to spend on chocolate. Maxi bars cost 30p
each and Giant bars cost 60p each. Elisa wishes to buy some of each of the
bars. If she buys x bars of Maxi and y bars of Giant, obtain an inequality in x
and y. Illustrate the inequality with a graph.

Solution

$$30x + 60y \leqslant 600 \quad \text{(in pence)}$$
$$3x + 6y \leqslant 60$$
$$x + 2y \leqslant 20$$

(This is obviously a straight line
graph. If $x = 0$, then $y = 10$ and if
$y = 0$ then $x = 20$ are two very
obvious points. Also neither x nor y
can be negative. It seems obvious
that Elisa could buy nothing so $(0, 0)$
is on the required side of the line.)

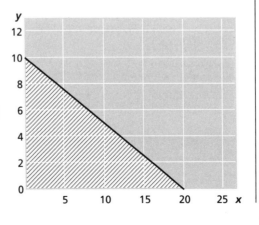

4

a Factorise the following, as far as possible:

    (i) p^2-q^2 (ii) c^2-1 (iii) $4-r^2$ (iv) $5-5$

    (v) x^2+x-6 (vi) $2x^2+5x-3$ (vii) $6a^2+11ab+5b^2$

Solution

(i) $p^2-q^2 = (p+q)(p-q)$

(ii) $c^2-1 = (c+1)(c-1)$

(iii) $4-r^2 = (2+r)(2-r)$

(iv) $5-5t^2 = 5(1-t^2) = 5(1+t)(1-t)$

    (Notice how the above are all the difference of two squares.)

(v) $x^2+x-6 = (x+3)(x-2)$

    (Think carefully what factors of 6 can give a 1 when added/subtracted.)

(vi) $2x^2+5x-3 = (2x-1)(x+3)$

    (One sign must be positive and the other negative to give a -3. Since 3 can only be the product of 1 and 3, try both possible ways: $+1$ and -3, and -1 and $+3$.)

(vii) $6a^2+11ab+5b^2 = (6a+5b)(a+b)$

    (The $6a^2$ could be either $3a$ and $2a$ or $6a$ and a. The $5b^2$ can only be $5b$ and b. So use trial and error until it works!)

b Complete the square for each of the following:

    (i) x^2-2x+7

    (ii) a^2+4a+2

    (iii) x^2-3x+1

Solution

(i)
$$\begin{aligned} x^2-2x+7 &= x^2-2x &&+7 \\ &= x^2-2x+1 &&+7-1 \\ &= (x-1)^2+6 \end{aligned}$$

(ii)
$$\begin{aligned} a^2+4a+2 &= a^2+4a &&+2 \\ &= a^2+4a+4 &&+2-4 \\ &= (a+2)^2-2 \end{aligned}$$

(iii) $\quad x^2 - 3x + 1 = x^2 - 3x \qquad\quad + 1$
$$= x^2 - 3x + (1.5)^2 \quad +1 - (1.5)^2$$
$$= (x - 1.5)^2 - 1.25$$

a Solve the following quadratic equations by factorising:

    (i) $(3x - 4)(x + 3) = 0$

    (ii) $m^2 + 4m - 32 = 0$

    (iii) $3x^2 - 7x + 2 = 0$

Solution

(i) $\quad (3x - 4)(x + 3) = 0$

    either $\quad 3x - 4 = 0$
$$x = \frac{4}{3}$$

    or $\quad x + 3 = 0$
$$x = -3$$

(ii) $\quad m^2 + 4m - 32 = 0$
$$(m + 8)(m - 4) = 0$$

    either
$$m + 8 = 0$$
$$m = -8$$

    or
$$m - 4 = 0$$
$$m = 4$$

(iii) $\quad 3x^2 - 7x + 2 = 0$
$$(3x - 1)(x - 2) = 0$$

    either
$$x - 2 = 0$$
$$x = 2$$

    or
$$3x - 1 = 0$$
$$x = \frac{1}{3}$$

b By completing the square solve the equation

$$x^2 - 8x + 2 = 0$$

Solution

$$x^2 - 8x + 2 = 0$$
$$x^2 - 8x = -2$$
$$x^2 - 8x + (4)^2 = -2 + (4)^2$$
$$(x-4)^2 = 14$$
$$x - 4 = \pm 3.74$$
$$x = 4 + 3.74 \text{ or } 4 - 3.74$$
$$x = 7.74 \text{ or } 0.26$$

c Using the formula, solve the following quadratic equation:

$$-2x^2 + 3x + 7 = 0$$

Solution

In this case as the coefficient of x^2 is negative we make it a little easier by multiplying both sides by -1:

$$2x^2 - 3x - 7 = 0$$

Using the formula:

$$x = \frac{-b \pm \sqrt{b^2 - 4ac}}{2a}$$

in our case $\quad a = 2, b = -3$ and $c = -7$:

$$x = \frac{-(-3) \pm \sqrt{(-3)^2 - 4(2)(-7)}}{2(2)}$$

$$= \frac{3 \pm \sqrt{9 + 56}}{4}$$

$$= \frac{3 \pm \sqrt{65}}{4}$$

$$= 2.77 \text{ or } 1.27 \quad \text{(to 3 s.f.)}$$

6 Solve the following pair of simultaneous equations:

$$2x + 3y = 15 \quad \text{(A)}$$
$$3x - 2y = 3 \quad \text{(B)}$$

Solution

$2 \times$ A and $3 \times$ B:

$$4x + 6y = 30 \qquad \text{(C)}$$
$$9x - 6y = 9 \qquad \text{(D)}$$

C + D:

$$13x = 39$$
$$x = 3$$

substitute in A

$$2(3) + 3y = 15$$
$$6 + 3y = 15$$
$$3y = 9$$
$$y = 3$$

7 When the price of admission to Dave's Disco rises by £1.00, the takings increase from £900 to £1000, but the attendance drops by 50. Given that the new price of admission is £x, obtain expressions in terms of x for:

(i) the old price of admission

(ii) the old attendance

(iii) the new attendance

Hence obtain an equation for x and solve it to find the new price of admission.

Solution

(i) The old price of admission is £1.00 less than the new, so

old price $=$ £$(x - 1)$

(ii) The old price produced £900 is takings, so

$$\text{old attendance} = \frac{900}{x - 1}$$

(iii) The new attendance produced £1000 in takings, so

$$\text{new attendance} = \frac{1000}{x}$$

To get the equation, we know that the new attendance is 50 less than the old attendance, so

$$\frac{900}{x-1} - 50 = \frac{1000}{x}$$

Solving this:

$$\frac{900}{x-1} - \frac{1000}{x} = 50$$

Multiplying both sides by $x(x-1)$ gives:

$$900x - 1000(x-1) = 50x(x-1)$$
$$900x - 1000x + 1000 = 50x^2 - 50x$$

Since it is a quadratic equation bring everything over to one side.

$$50x^2 - 50x + 100x - 1000 = 0$$
$$50x^2 + 50x - 1000 = 0$$

Divide both sides by 50

$$x^2 + x - 20 = 0$$

Factorise

$$(x+5)(x-4) = 0$$

so

$$x = -5 \text{ or } 4$$

Since the value of x is the price of admission, the only answer that fits the problem is $x = 4$.

If the new price is £4.00, the old price was £3.00.

The old attendance figure is $\dfrac{900}{3} = 300$.

The new attendance figure is $\dfrac{1000}{4} = 250$.

The difference in attendance is 50, so we have found the solution to the problem: the new price is £4.00.

Do It Yourself

1 Simplify:

(i) $2c - c + 4c$ (ii) $4t \times 3t$ (iii) $x^9 \div x^4$

2a If $a = 3$, $b = 2$, $c = 1$ and $d = 5$, find the value of:

(i) $5a + 2b - c - d$

(ii) $\dfrac{a + 2b + 3c + 4d}{abcd}$

(iii) $\sqrt{ad + c}$

(iv) $(b + 2d)^2 - a^2$

b Solve the following equations:

(i) $\dfrac{3x - 4}{5} = 4$ (ii) $3 - x = 6 + 2x$

(iii) $6(x + 1) + 7 = -5$

3 Isha wanted to buy oranges at 15p each and grapefruit at 20p each. She must buy at least one grapefruit and her basket cannot hold more than five fruits. By letting x be the number of oranges bought and y the number of grapefruit bought, answer the following:

(i) Write down three inequalities.
(ii) Draw these on graph paper.
(iii) What possible combinations of oranges and grapefruit might Isha buy?

4 Factorise:

(i) $3xy - 6xz$
(ii) $100x^2 - 9$
(iii) $a^2 + 8a + 15$
(iv) $x^2 + 10x + 25$

5 **a** Solve the following quadratic equations in the most appropriate way:

(i) $(x+1)(x-3) = 0$

(ii) $x^2 + 7x + 10 = 0$

(iii) $x^2 - 5x = 0$

(iv) $(x+3)^2 = 25$

b A quadratic equation gave the solution $x = 2$ or $x = -9$. What was its equation?

6 Solve the following pairs of simultaneous equations:

(i) $3x + 2y = 7$

$x - 5y = -9$

(ii) $4x - 3y = 15$

$5x + 2y = 13$

7 A rectangular hall is 4 metres wider than it is high and it is 8 metres longer than it is wide. The total area of the walls is 512 m². Using x for the height of the hall in metres, write down expressions for:

(i) the width of the hall

(ii) the length of the hall

(iii) the area of each of the walls

Form an equation and solve it to find the dimensions of the hall.

Answers

Section 1

1a (i) 9300, 100, 200 (ii) 9330, 85.5, 227 (iii) 9326.69, 85.51, 227.25

b (i) 2.65 (ii) 6.63 (iii) 0.556
(iv) 11.6

2 (i) -4 (ii) -14 (iii) 9
(iv) -2 (v) 28 (vi) -7
(vii) 50 (viii) 14 (ix) -240
(x) $3\frac{3}{4}$

3a (i) 2^5 (ii) 4^7 (iii) 3^2
(iv) 2^6 (v) 3^6 (vi) 2^{13}
(vii) 9^{17} or 3^{34} (viii) 2^7

b (i) $n = 5$ (ii) 0.0041

c (i) $\frac{1}{5}$ (ii) $\frac{1}{8}$ (iii) 1
(iv) 3 or -3 (v) 2 (vi) $\frac{1}{6}$ or $\frac{1}{-6}$

d (i) 1.5×10^{-2} (ii) 12×10^2 or 1.2×10^3

4 (i) 5.971×10^3 (ii) 7.8×10^4 (iii) 3.52×10^{-3}
(iv) 1.4×10^7

Section 2

1 (i) 3 (ii) 10, 15 (iii) 1, 10

2a $35^2 = 30 \times 40 + 25 = 1225$
$45^2 = 40 \times 50 + 25 = 2025$
$55^2 = 50 \times 60 + 25 = 3025$
$65^2 = 60 \times 70 + 25 = 4225$
$75^2 = 70 \times 80 + 25 = 5625$
$85^2 = 80 \times 90 + 25 = 7225$
$95^2 = 90 \times 1000 + 25 = 9025$

b The two triangular numbers are 6 and 5. It is not difficult to see that any square number can be made up of two triangular numbers in the same way. If we have the nth square number then we have the relationship

$$S_n = T_n + T_{n-1}$$

where S_n means the nth square number and T_n and T_{n-1} the nth and $(n-1)$th triangular numbers.

3 Since this relies upon the number that is being cubed also being a square number, we get the answer 9^3 or 729 ($27^2 = 729$).

4a The difference is always 1 – e.g. consider

8   13   21

$8 \times 21 = 168$, $13^2 = 169$.

b $n = 1$ gives 9 $n = 2$ gives 13
$n = 3$ gives 17 $n = 4$ gives 21
$n = 5$ gives 25 $n = 6$ gives 29
$n = 7$ gives 33 $n = 8$ gives 37

The square numbers are for $n = 1$ and $n = 5$, i.e. 9 and 25.

5 a (i) 15, 18   (ii) 16, 19   (iii) 20, 25
(iv) 8, 5

b 0.5, 0.6666 . . ., 0.75, 0.8, 0.833 333 . . .

It is a value that is close to 1 as the values are all getting larger, but obviously the numerator of the fraction will never be larger than the denominator. It actually works out as 100/101 or 0.990 099.

c If $x^3 - 2x - 5 = 0$, then

$$x^3 = 2x + 5$$

dividing by x gives

$$x^2 = 2 + \frac{5}{x}$$

Square rooting gives the required answer.

$x_1 = 2$ gives the next value of x as 2.121 3203
$x_2 = 2.121\,3203$ gives the next value of x as 2.087 3482
$x_3 = 2.087\,3482$ gives the next value of x as 2.096 5171
$x_4 = 2.096\,5171$ gives the next value of x as 2.094 0172
$x_5 = 2.094\,0172$ gives the next value of x as 2.094 6969

The value of x is 2.09 correct to two decimal places.

d (i) $x_1 = 3$ gives $x_2 = 6$
$x_2 = 6$ gives $x_3 = 5.5$
$x_3 = 5.5$ gives $x_4 = 5.363\,6364$
(ii) $x_4 = 5.363\,6364$ gives $x_5 = 5.559\,322$
$x_5 = 5.559\,322$ gives $x_6 = 5.539\,6341$
$x_6 = 5.539\,6341$ gives $x_7 = 5.541\,552$
$x_7 = 5.541\,552$ gives $x_8 = 5.541\,3646$
$x_8 = 5.541\,3646$ gives $x_9 = 5.541\,3829$

A value of x is 5.54 correct to two decimal places.

Section 3

1 a (i) $\frac{3}{8}$ and $\frac{5}{8}$ (ii) $\frac{4}{9}$ and $\frac{5}{9}$ (iii) $\frac{1}{2}$ and $\frac{1}{2}$
(iv) $\frac{1}{2}$ and $\frac{1}{2}$

b $\frac{3}{4}$ $\frac{1}{3}$ $\frac{3}{10}$ $\frac{2}{9}$ $\frac{2}{5}$ $\frac{1}{2}$

c $\frac{1}{8}$ $\frac{1}{4}$ $\frac{5}{16}$ $\frac{3}{8}$ $\frac{7}{16}$ $\frac{1}{2}$ $\frac{9}{16}$ $\frac{5}{8}$ $\frac{11}{16}$ $\frac{3}{4}$ $\frac{7}{8}$

2 (i) $\frac{13}{15}$ (ii) $\frac{17}{20}$ (iii) $\frac{16}{35}$
(iv) $\frac{5}{18}$

3 (i) $\frac{1}{6}$ (ii) $\frac{5}{9}$

4 (i) $\frac{10}{3}$ or $3\frac{1}{3}$ (ii) $\frac{25}{32}$

5 (i) $\frac{6}{11}$ (ii) $\frac{1}{9}$

Section 4

1 a £46.75

b £22.20 (to the nearest penny)

c (i) £233.83 (to nearest penny)   (ii) £105.75
(iii) £37.01 (to nearest penny)

d (i) £21.27 (to nearest penny)
(ii) £34.03 (to nearest penny)
(iii) £21.28 (to nearest penny)
(iv) £46.81 (to nearest penny)

e (i) just under 100.5 m   (ii) 99.5 m
(iii) just under 13.25 seconds   (iv) 13.15 seconds

Using 100.5 m as the maximum distance the maximum average speed = 7.64 m/second.

f Dealer sold it for £6000, buyer sold it back for £4800.

2 a (i) £18 : £27   (ii) 24 m : 18 m
(iii) 14 kg : 21 kg : 28 kg

b 0.8 kg or 800 g

Section 5

(i) £225
(ii) £9000 (over 10 years £27 000 is paid back)

a £96

b 5 years

Simple interest earns £150, compound interest earns £132.40. So the simple interest is the better investment by £17.60.

Section 6

The answer by calculation is 283.56 m. By drawing, an answer of about 280 m is acceptable.

500 m²

Height = 3 m, floor area = 10.9375 m²,
volume = 32.8125 m³.

Approximately 252 m at a bearing of 308°.

Section 7

1 a (i) 7.431 kg   (ii) 0.3761 kg   (iii) 4500 kg

b 34.5 kg

c 0.7 mg   700 mg   70 g   0.7 kg

d 650 g

e £29.70

2 a (i) 46 mm   (ii) 79 mm   (iii) 9100 mm
(iv) 31200 mm

b (i) 500 cm   (ii) 920 cm   (iii) 74 cm
(iv) 643.1 cm

c (i) 0.8 km   (ii) 0.004 km   (iii) 0.000 65 km
(iv) 0.021 km

d Each sheet weighs 6 g, thickness = 0.14 mm.

3 14.2 centilitres

Section 8

1 a (i) 168.7 cm (1 d.p.)   (ii) 169 cm   (iii) 162 cm

b (i) 2 goals   (ii) $1\frac{1}{2}$ goals   (iii) 0 goals

c (i) mean = 1.71 metres
standard deviation = 0.0789 m (or 7.89 cm)
(ii) As the standard deviation for the Rovers team is the larger and the means for the teams are close, it is likely that Rovers have the tallest player.

2 (i)

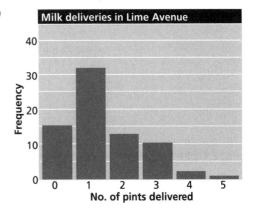

(ii) 73   (iii) 58   (iv) 101

159

3

No. of letters	1	2	3	4	5	6	7	8	9	10	11	12
Frequency	3	1	3	0	1	3	0	5	5	5	2	2

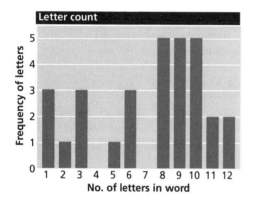

4 a

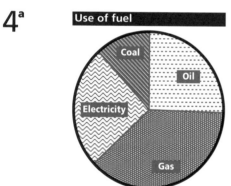

b UK – £2 700 000   Denmark – £1 800 000
Israel – £450 000   USA – £1 125 000
Germany – £2 025 000

c

5

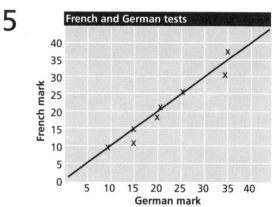

The estimate of his German mark is 17.

6

	1	1	1	2	2	3
1	2	2	2	3	3	4
2	3	3	3	4	4	5
3	4	4	4	5	5	6
3	4	4	4	5	5	6
5	6	6	6	7	7	8
5	6	6	6	7	7	8

(i) $\frac{8}{36}$ or $\frac{2}{9}$
(ii) $\frac{7}{36}$
(iii) Trish – there are more ways of getting 4.

7 (i) $\frac{5}{100}$ or $\frac{1}{20}$ or 0.05 (ii) $\frac{85}{99}$

8 **a** (i) $\frac{5}{12}$
(ii) $\frac{1}{12}$
(iii) $\frac{1}{4}$
(iv) $\frac{1}{2}$

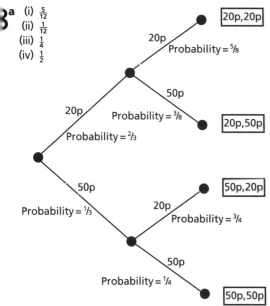

b (i) $\frac{1}{8}$
(ii) $\frac{3}{8}$

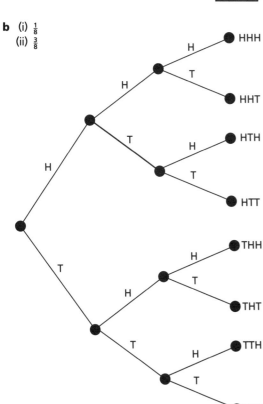

Section 9

1 (i) $y = 3x + 4$ (ii) $y = -2x - 2$
(iii) $y = -\frac{1}{2}x + 3$ or $2y = -x + 6$
(iv) $y = 4x - 6$ (v) $y = -x - \frac{1}{4}$ or $4y = -4x - 1$

2 **a** (i) gradient is 4, y-axis intercept is -7
(ii) gradient is 2, y-axis intercept is 9
(iii) gradient is 6, y-axis intercept is 3
(iv) gradient is 5, y-axis intercept is $-\frac{1}{2}$
(v) gradient is $\frac{1}{4}$, y-axis intercept is -2
(vi) gradient is -1, y-axis intercept is 8

b (i) gradient $= 1$ (ii) AB $= 7.07$ units
(iii) $y = x - 3$

3

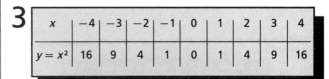

x	-4	-3	-2	-1	0	1	2	3	4
$y = x^2$	16	9	4	1	0	1	4	9	16

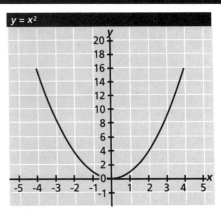

$1.8^2 = 3.2$, square root of $13 = 3.6$.

4

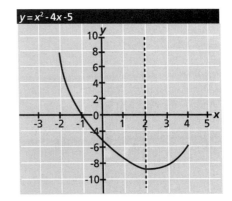

161

5 Gradient when $x = -1$ is -4.
Gradient when $x = 2$ is 8.

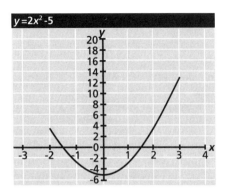

6a (i) $x = 1, y = 1$ (ii) $x = \frac{1}{2}, y = -2\frac{1}{2}$
(iii) $x = -2, y = 1$

b $x = 2.4$ or -0.4

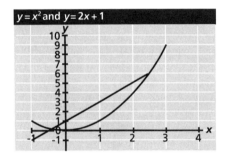

c $x = 1.6$

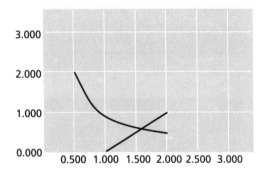

7a The coach arrives at 18.05.
Average speed = 57.6 miles/hour.

b (i) 9.20 a.m.   (ii) 40.1 miles/hour

c (i) 10 minutes   (ii) 4 minutes
(iii) 1000 m or 1 km   (iv) 2000 m or 2 km

d (i)

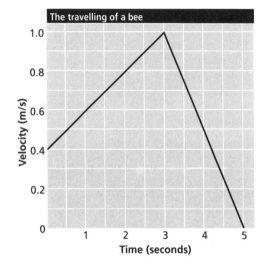

(ii) (a) $0.2\,\text{m/s}^2$
(b) $-0.5\,\text{m/s}^2$

e (i) 38 km
(ii)

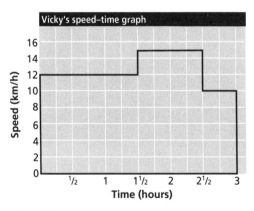

(iii) $12\frac{2}{3}\,\text{km/h}$

ection 10

(i) Magnitude 5 miles, direction is north-east.
(ii) Magnitude 3 kg, direction downward.
(iii) Magnitude 40 m, direction south-west.

$\overrightarrow{AB}$ is $\begin{pmatrix} 2 \\ 1 \end{pmatrix}$ $\overrightarrow{AC}$ is $\begin{pmatrix} -2 \\ -8 \end{pmatrix}$ $\overrightarrow{CD}$ is $\begin{pmatrix} 6 \\ 3 \end{pmatrix}$ $\overrightarrow{BD}$ is $\begin{pmatrix} 2 \\ -4 \end{pmatrix}$

$\overrightarrow{DA}$ is $\begin{pmatrix} -4 \\ 3 \end{pmatrix}$

AB and CD are parallel.

(i) Vector is $\begin{pmatrix} -2 \\ 2 \end{pmatrix}$, modulus is 2.8 units.

(ii) Vector is $\begin{pmatrix} 4 \\ -2 \end{pmatrix}$, modulus is 4.47 units.

(iii) Vector is $\begin{pmatrix} -2 \\ 0 \end{pmatrix}$, modulus is 2 units.

$\overrightarrow{AB}$ is $\begin{pmatrix} 3 \\ 6 \end{pmatrix}$ $\overrightarrow{CD}$ is $\begin{pmatrix} 1 \\ 2 \end{pmatrix}$ so they are parallel (same

ratios). Their lengths are in the ratio 3 : 1. No, the four
points do not form a parallelogram.

(i) $\mathbf{x} = \begin{pmatrix} 3 \\ 5 \end{pmatrix}$, $\mathbf{y} = \begin{pmatrix} 7 \\ -3 \end{pmatrix}$.

(ii) $\begin{pmatrix} 20 \\ 4 \end{pmatrix}$ and $\begin{pmatrix} 20 \\ 4 \end{pmatrix}$.

(iii) $\begin{pmatrix} 5 \\ 1 \end{pmatrix}$; yes, it is the vector $\overrightarrow{OM}$.

a $\mathbf{f}+\mathbf{g} = \begin{pmatrix} 5 \\ 12 \end{pmatrix}$

8.25, 5, 13

b Actual speed is 5.83 km/h at an angle of 31°
downstream to going straight across.

(i) $\begin{pmatrix} -10 \\ -10 \end{pmatrix}$ and (ii) $\begin{pmatrix} -10 \\ -10 \end{pmatrix}$.

a D could be (2, 2) – it could also be at (0, 0).

b $\overrightarrow{LM} = \begin{pmatrix} 4 \\ 2 \end{pmatrix}$, $\overrightarrow{NP} = \begin{pmatrix} -4 \\ -2 \end{pmatrix}$. These are parallel and equal
in length, so it is a parallelogram.
    L to N = 5 units; M to P = 5 units. Since diagonals
are equal and it is a parallelogram the shape must be a
rectangle.

Section 11

1 $a = 132°, b = 65°, c = 42°, d = 83°, e = 55°, f = 60°,$
$g = 45°, h = 120°$

2 a The ship is in danger for about 27 minutes (the length
of path in danger is 4.47 miles).

b The curve looks like:

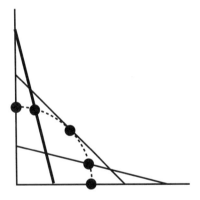

Section 12

1 $a = 35°, b = 76°$

2 The length of XZ is 8.7 cm and the length of YZ is 5 cm.

3 **a** $c = 115°$ $d = 65°$ $e = 65°$

b The other angles are each 130°. The shape might be a parallelogram.

4 **a** (i) 36°   (ii) 144°

b (i) 12 sides   (ii) 150°

5 **a** AC = 16.97 cm, AD = 20.78 cm

b (Joining the centres produces an isosceles triangle – height is 10.58 cm) height of gift pack = 20 cm, length of gift pack = 48 cm, width of gift pack = 26.58 cm.

6 **a** (i) $x = 34.8°$ (ii) $y = 26.6°$ (iii) $z = 49°$

b (i) $x = 3$ cm   (ii) $y = 6.3$ cm   (iii) $z = 14.1$ cm

c Height of pole = 5.36 m (2 d.p.)
Angle of elevation = 1.8°

Section 13

1 See chapter for diagrams.

2 **a** Distance = 8.64 cm

b Radius = 4.45 cm

c 31.4 m

d 11 207 mm² or 112.1 cm²

e 23 836 mm² or 238.4 cm²

3 **a** Each line is a tangent to the circle so from A to each of the points of contact is the same distance (call it a), similarly for all the other three points. So

$$AB = a+b \quad CD = c+d \quad BC = b+c \quad AD = a+$$

Thus

$$AB + CD = a+b+c+d$$

and

$$BC + AD = a+b+c+d$$

b The angles are 54°, 56° and 70°. (Look at Things You Need to Know 3: ix. Find the rest of the angles at the points of contact. Remember that the lengths of the tangents from an external point to the points of conta are the same.)

Section 14

1

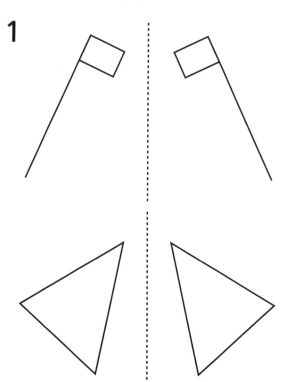

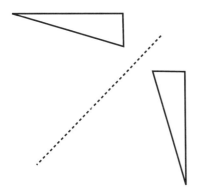

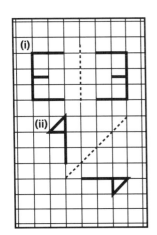

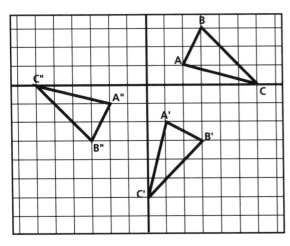

5 (i) A'(6, 2)   B'(7, −1)   C'(5, −1)   D'(5, 1)
(ii) original coordinates of:
   A(−1, 3)   B(0, 0)   C(−2, 0)   D(−2, 2)

Translation was $\begin{pmatrix} 4 \\ 1 \end{pmatrix}$.

6
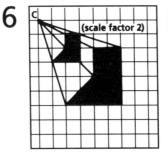
(scale factor 2)

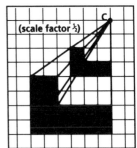
(scale factor ½)

7 A rotation of 180°.

8 Write the matrix **X** as $\begin{pmatrix} a & b \\ c & d \end{pmatrix}$ then multiply the coordinates of points and compare the results.

$$\mathbf{X} = \begin{pmatrix} 2 & 1 \\ 3 & 2 \end{pmatrix}$$

4 There are many possible answers here – all easy to check by tracing and rotating the shape you have on top of itself.

Section 15

1 Try out your answers on someone else – see whether they can identify the shape from your description.

2 (i) a triangular prism   (ii) a cuboid
(iii) a square-based pyramid
(iv) a tetrahedron or a triangular pyramid

3 a (i) perimeter = 16 cm
(ii) the unshaded area = 6.25 cm²
(iii) the shaded area = 9.75 cm²
(iv) the width of the band = 2.12 cm

b 67.36 cm²

165

c As volume is 64 cm³ the length of side must be 4 cm, so surface area = 96 cm².

d 6 cm²

4 **a** (i) (radius of gully is 2.5 cm) Cross-sectional area = 140.2 cm²
 (ii) volume = 5607 cm³
 (iii) mass = 33.6 kg

 b 7330 cm³

Section 16

1 (i) 5c (ii) 12t² (iii) x⁵

2 **a** (i) 13 (ii) 1 (iii) 4 or −4
 (iv) 135

 b (i) $x = 8$ (ii) $x = -1$ (iii) $x = -3$

3 (i) $y \geqslant 1, x > 0, x + y \leqslant 5.$
 (ii)

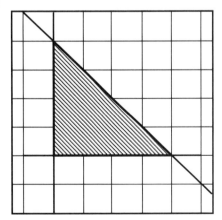

 (iii) 1 grapefruit with 0, 1, 2, 3 or 4 oranges
 2 grapefruit with 0, 1, 2 or 3 oranges
 3 grapefruit with 0, 1 or 2 oranges
 4 grapefruit with 0 or 1 orange
 just 5 grapefruit

4 (i) $3x(y - 2z)$ (ii) $(10x - 3)(10x + 3)$
 (iii) $(a + 3)(a + 5)$ (iv) $(x + 5)^2$

5 **a** (i) $x = -1$ or 3 (ii) $x = -2$ or -5
 (iii) $x = 0$ or 5 (iv) $x = -8$ or 2

 b There are many forms for it, one possible is

 $$(x - 2)(x + 9) = 0$$

 In the standard layout it would be

 $$x^2 + 7x - 18 = 0$$

6 (i) $x = 1, y = 2$ (ii) $x = 3, y = -1$

7 (i) $x + 4$ (ii) $x + 12$ (iii) $x^2 + 4x, x^2 + 12x$

 Equation is

 $$2(x^2 + 4x) + 2(x^2 + 12x) = 512$$
 $$x = 8 \text{ or } -16 \quad (-16 \text{ is silly for the height})$$

 Dimensions are height = 8 m, width = 12 m, length = 20 m.

Sample Exam Paper

1 (i) Estimate the value of

$$\frac{9.37 \times \sqrt{89.5}}{(0.9)^2 + 7.3}$$

correct to one significant figure, explaining clearly how you obtained your answer.

(ii) Evaluate the expression to three significant figures using your calculator.

2 The distance d metres travelled by an object in t seconds is given by the formula

$$d = 4t^2 - 6t + 11$$

(i) Find d if $t = 3.7$.

(ii) Find the values of t for which $d = 9$.

3 In a science experiment, Jason had measured three different lengths a, b, c. He used these measurements to find the surface area of the object he was measuring, by substituting into the formula

$$A = 4ab + 3ac + 6bc + abc$$

His friend Carl said that he must have miscopied the formula. Explain why.

4 Find the largest integer which is a solution of the inequality

$$4(2x - 7) \leqslant 9$$

5 A survey of salaries in a factory gave the following results:

24 assistants earning	£8500 each
12 middle managers earning	£12 000 each
2 managers earning	£15 000 each
3 directors earning	£22 000 each

From these data, find:

    (i) the mode;
    (ii) the median;
    (iii) the mean.

Which of these values best describes the data? Explain carefully your answer.

6 The total cost of five shirts and two jumpers is £116. The total cost of eight identical shirts and three identical jumpers is £182. What is the cost of one shirt and one jumper?

7 (i) Calculate: (a) $5^{1/2}$ (b) $28^{-1/3}$
   (ii) If $2^N > 10^8$, find the smallest integer value of N for which this is true.

8 A framework in the shape of a cube is made from straws of length 6 cm each. Referring to the diagram, calculate:

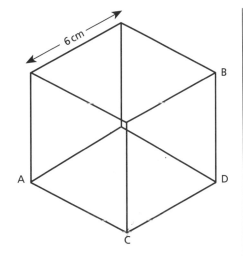

    (i) angle ABC;
    (ii) the volume of the
        pyramid ABDC.

9 State with a reason whether each of the following numbers are rational or irrational:

    (i) $\sqrt{5}$ (ii) $0.\dot{4}$ (iii) $\sqrt{12} \div \sqrt{3}$
    (iv) π

10 A boat sets out from A and travels 8 nautical miles due north to B. It then changes course and sails on a bearing of 068° for a further 12 nautical miles to point C. It then changes course again, and returns to A.

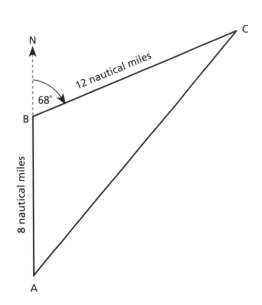

Calculate:
 (i) the distance AC;
 (ii) the bearing of A from C.
If the boat averages a speed of 4 knots (1 knot = 1 nautical mile/hour), calculate to the nearest minute the time taken to complete the journey ABCA.

11 The marks of 90 students in an IQ test are summarised in the table on the right:

IQ	Frequency
71–90	2
91–110	15
111–130	46
131–150	24
151–170	3

(i) Draw up a cumulative frequency table for these results, and plot on suitably labelled axes the cumulative frequency curve.

(ii) Find the interquartile range.

(iii) What is the probability that a pupil chosen at random has an IQ of more than 120?

(iv) By using midpoint values, calculate an estimate for the average IQ of the group.

12 On a single diagram, draw a sketch showing the graphs of $y = 2x^3$, and $y = 10 - x$. What does your diagram tell you about the solution of the equation

$$2x^3 + x - 10 = 0$$

Find the solution of this equation by trial and improvement, correct to one decimal place.

The equation can also be solved by using the iteration

$$x_{n+1} = \sqrt{\frac{5}{x_n} - \frac{1}{2}}$$

Starting with $x_0 = 1.6$, find the solution to the equation correct to two decimal places. What do you notice about this iteration?

13 Find the standard deviation of the numbers

8   11   12   16   20   23

4 In the diagram, CT is a tangent to the circle at T, O is the centre of the circle and ABC is a straight line. If ∠ACT = 20°, find ∠ADT, giving reasons.

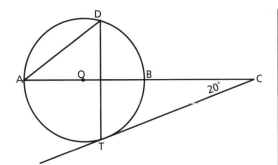

5 (i) Find the 2 × 2 matrix that represents reflection in the line $y = x$.

(ii) The matrix

$$\begin{pmatrix} a & b \\ c & d \end{pmatrix}$$

transforms the points A(1, 1) and B(2, 1) into A′(3, 4) and B′(−1, 0) respectively. Find the values of a, b, c and d.

6 Simplify:

    (i) $(6x^2)^2 \div 3x$ (ii) $(8x^6)^{2/3}$

    (iii) $\dfrac{2x}{3} + \dfrac{x-4}{6}$ (iv) $\dfrac{1}{x+2} - \dfrac{1}{x-3}$

7 Plot the graph of $y = 4\sin 2x° + 6$, for values of x between 0° and 180°. Use your graph to solve the equation

    $4\sin 2x = -2$ for $0° \leqslant x \leqslant 180°$

Solutions

1 (i) $\dfrac{9.37 \times \sqrt{89.5}}{(0.9)^2 + 7.3} \approx \dfrac{9 \times 9}{1 + 7} = \dfrac{81}{8} \approx 10$　　(ii) 10.9

2 (i) $d = 4(3.7)^2 - 6(3.7) + 11 = 43.56$
(ii)　$4t^2 - 6t + 11 = 9$
　　　$4t^2 - 6t + 2 = 0$
　　Divide by 2:
　　　$2t^2 - 3t + 1 = 0$　(guessing is not sufficient)
　　　$(2t - 1)(t - 1) = 0$
　　$\therefore \ t = 0.5$ or 1

3 The $+abc$ part must be wrong, because multiplying three lengths would give a volume, not an area.

4 $8x - 28 \leqslant 9$　　$\therefore \ 8x \leqslant 37$　　Hence $x \leqslant 4\frac{5}{8}$
The largest integer will be 4.

5 (i) £8500
(ii) There are 41 people, and so the median will be the 21st salary if arranged in order of size. This will also be £8500.
(iii) The mean $= £(24 \times 8500 + 12 \times 12\,000 + 2$
　　　　　　$\times 15\,000 + 3 \times 22\,000) \div 41$
　　　　$= £10\,830$
The mean is weighted by a few higher salaries; also, £8500 is a repeated value, so £8500 is the best measure of the average earnings.

6 If £x is the cost of one shirt, and £y the cost of one jumper, then

　　　　　　$5x + 2y = 116$ ①

　　　　　　$8x + 3y = 182$ ②

　① × 3　$15x + 6y = 348$ ③

　② × 2　$16x + 6y = 364$ ④

　④ − ③　　　$x = 16$

　　Substitute in ①:

　　　　　$80 + 2y = 116$
　　　　　$\therefore \ y = 18$

　The shirt costs £16, the jumper £18.

7 (i) (a) 2.24　　(b) 0.329
(ii) Since $10^8 = 100\,000\,000$, if you start looking at $2^1 = 2$, $2^2 = 4$, $2^3 = 8$, the first value of N for which 2^N exceeds $100\,000\,000$ is $N = 27$.

8 (i) You need to realise that $\triangle ACB$ is right angled.
　　　$BC = \sqrt{6^2 + 6^2} = \sqrt{72}$
　　Hence $\tan ABC = \dfrac{6}{\sqrt{72}}$
　　giving angle $ABC = 35.3°$

(ii) Volume of a pyramid $= \frac{1}{3}$ (base area × height)
　　Base area $ADC = \frac{1}{2} \times 6 \times 6 = 18$ cm²
　　$\therefore$ Volume $= \frac{1}{3} \times 18 \times 6 = 36$ cm³

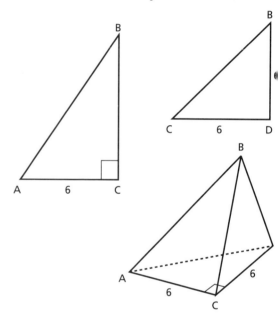

9 (i) irrational, not a fraction　　(ii) rational, $= \frac{4}{9}$;
(iii) $\sqrt{12} \div \sqrt{3} = \sqrt{12 \div 3} = 2$, hence rational;
(iv) irrational, π cannot be written as a fraction.

10 (i) Using the cosine rule
　　　　$AC^2 = 8^2 + 12^2 - 2 \times 8 \times 12 \cos 112°$
　　　　　　$= 279.9$
　　　　$\therefore \ AC = 16.7$ nautical miles

(ii) Using the sine rule
　　　$\dfrac{\sin C}{8} = \dfrac{\sin 112°}{16.7}$
　　$\therefore \ \sin C = \dfrac{8 \sin 112°}{16.7} = 0.4442$
　　$\therefore \ C = 26.4°$

The bearing $= 360° - 112° - 26.4°$

$= 221.6°$

The total distance $= 8 + 12 + 16.7$

$= 36.7$ nautical miles

The time $= \dfrac{36.7}{4}$ hours

$= 9$ hours 10 minutes

1

(i) Cumulative frequencies are 2, 17, 63, 87, 90.

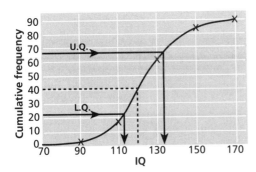

(ii) Interquartile range $=$ UQ $-$ LQ

$= 134 - 112 = 22$

(iii) $\dfrac{(90-40)}{90} = \dfrac{5}{9}$

(iv) $(2 \times 80.5 + 15 \times 100.5 + 46 \times 120.5$
$+ 24 \times 140.5 + 3 \times 160.5) \div 90 = 122.9$

2 Diagram shows there is only one solution, about $x = 2$.

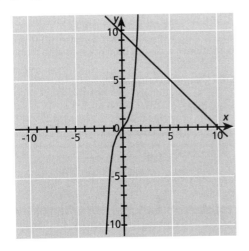

Try $x = 3$ $2 \times 3^3 + 3 - 10 = 47$ too high

$x = 2$ $2 \times 2^3 + 2 - 10 = 8$ too high

$x = 1.5$ $2 \times 1.5^3 + 1.5 - 10 = -1.75$ too low

$x = 1.6$ $2 \times 1.6^3 + 1.6 - 10 = -0.208$ too low

$x = 1.7$ $2 \times 1.7^3 + 1.7 - 10 = 1.526$ too high

The solution is $x = 1.6$ to one decimal place.

$x_0 = 1.6$ $x_1 - 1.620$ $x_2 - 1.608$

$x_3 = 1.615$ $x_4\ 1.611$ $x_5 = 1.614$

The solution is 1.61 to two decimal places. This iteration converges quite slowly.

13 The mean $= 90 \div 6 = 15$

Standard deviation $= 12.8$

14 $\angle$OTC $= 90°$ angle between tangent and radius

$\angle$COT $= 90° - 20° = 70°$ angle sum of triangle

$\angle$TOA $= 180° - 70° = 110°$ angles on a straight line

$\angle$ADT $= \frac{1}{2} \times 110° = 55°$ angle at the centre equals

twice angle at circumference

15 (i) $\begin{pmatrix} 0 & 1 \\ 1 & 0 \end{pmatrix}$ (ii) $\begin{pmatrix} a & b \\ c & d \end{pmatrix}\begin{pmatrix} 1 & 2 \\ 1 & 1 \end{pmatrix} = \begin{pmatrix} 3 & -1 \\ 4 & 0 \end{pmatrix}$

$\therefore$ $a + b = 3$ and $2a + b = -1$

giving $a = -4$, $b = 7$.

$c + d = 4$ and $2c + d = 0$

giving $c = -4$, $d = 8$.

16 (i) $36x^4 \div 3x = 12x^3$

(ii) $8^{2/3} \times x^4 = 4x^4$

(iii) $\dfrac{4x + x - 4}{6} = \dfrac{5x - 4}{6}$

(iv) $\dfrac{(x-3) - (x+2)}{(x+2)(x-3)} = \dfrac{x - 3 - x - 2}{(x+2)(x-3)} = \dfrac{-5}{(x+2)(x-3)}$

17 If $4 \sin 2x = -2$ then $4 \sin 2x + 6 = 4$

Draw $y = 4$; required values of x are 105° and 165°.

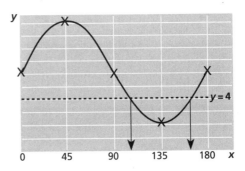

Index